Anatomy and Physiology
Ready Notes
Second Edition
Kenneth S. Saladin
Georgia College and State University

The McGraw-Hill Companies, Inc.
Primis Custom Publishing

New York St. Louis San Francisco Auckland Bogotá
Caracas Lisbon London Madrid Mexico Milan Montreal New Delhi Paris
San Juan Singapore Sydney Tokyo Toronto

McGraw-Hill Higher Education
*A Division of The **McGraw-Hill** Companies*

Anatomy and Physiology Ready Notes

2 3 4 5 6 7 8 9 0   QSR QSR   0 9 8 7 6 5 4 3 2 1

ISBN 0-07-250103-0

Printer/Binder: Quebecor World

TABLE OF CONTENTS

Chapter 1

Anatomy and Physiology: The Unity of Form and Function
Second Edition

Kenneth S. Saladin

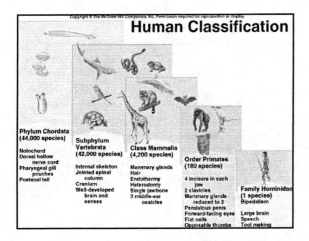

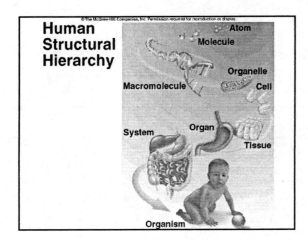

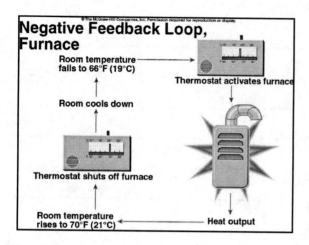

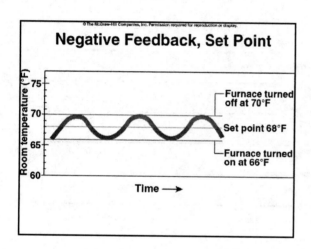

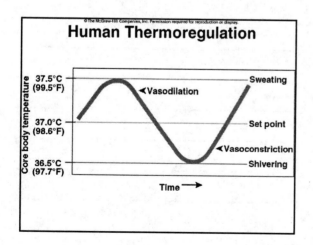

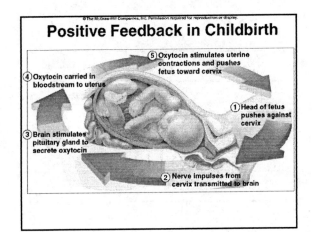

Positive Feedback in Childbirth

⑤ Oxytocin stimulates uterine contractions and pushes fetus toward cervix

④ Oxytocin carried in bloodstream to uterus

① Head of fetus pushes against cervix

③ Brain stimulates pituitary gland to secrete oxytocin

② Nerve impulses from cervix transmitted to brain

_____

_____

_____

_____

_____

_____

_____

Chapter 2

Anatomy and Physiology: The Unity of Form and Function
Second Edition

Kenneth S. Saladin

Planetary models of Elements(1)

First energy level

Second energy level

Hydrogen (H) $1p^+$
Atomic number = 1
Atomic mass = 1

Helium (He) $2p^+$, $2n^0$
Atomic number = 2
Atomic mass = 4

Carbon (C) $6p^+$, $6n^0$
Atomic number = 6
Atomic mass = 12

Nitrogen (N) $7p^+$, $7n^0$
Atomic number = 7
Atomic mass = 14

Planetary Models of Elements (2)

Third energy level

Fourth energy level

Oxygen (O) $8p^+$, $8n^0$
Atomic number = 8
Atomic mass = 16

Chlorine (Cl) $17p^+$, $18n^0$
Atomic number = 17
Atomic mass = 35

Sodium (Na) $11p^+$, $12n^0$
Atomic number = 11
Atomic mass = 23

Potassium (K) $19p^+$, $20n^0$
Atomic number = 19
Atomic mass = 39

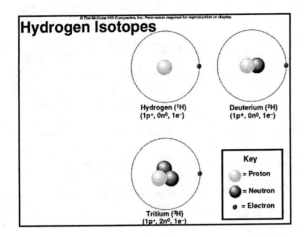

Hydrogen Isotopes

Hydrogen (^{1}H)
($1p^+$, $0n^0$, $1e^-$)

Deuterium (^{2}H)
($1p^+$, $0n^0$, $1e^-$)

Tritium (^{3}H)
($1p^+$, $2n^0$, $1e^-$)

Key
= Proton
= Neutron
= Electron

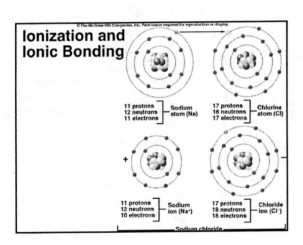

Ionization and Ionic Bonding

11 protons
12 neutrons
11 electrons — Sodium atom (Na)

17 protons
18 neutrons
17 electrons — Chlorine atom (Cl)

11 protons
12 neutrons
10 electrons — Sodium ion (Na$^+$)

17 protons
18 neutrons
18 electrons — Chloride ion (Cl$^-$)

Sodium chloride

Structural Isomers

	Structural formulae	Condensed structural formulae	Molecular formulae
Ethanol	H—C—C—OH (with H atoms)	CH_3CH_2OH	C_2H_6O
Ethyl ether	H—C—O—C—H (with H atoms)	CH_3OCH_3	C_2H_6O

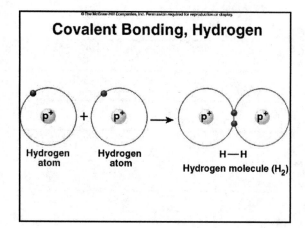

Covalent Bonding, Hydrogen

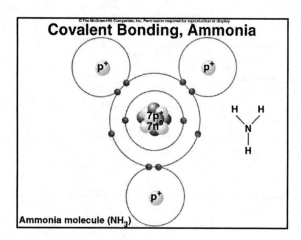

Covalent Bonding, Ammonia

Ammonia molecule (NH_3)

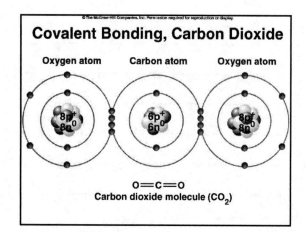

Covalent Bonding, Carbon Dioxide

Oxygen atom   Carbon atom   Oxygen atom

O═C═O
Carbon dioxide molecule (CO_2)

_____
_____
_____
_____
_____
_____
_____

_____
_____
_____
_____
_____
_____
_____

_____
_____
_____
_____
_____
_____
_____

Covalent Bonds, Nonpolar and Polar

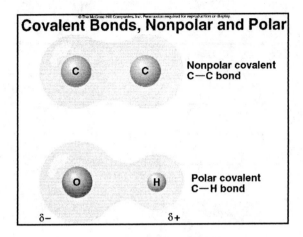

Nonpolar covalent
C—C bond

Polar covalent
C—H bond

$\delta-$ $\delta+$

Hydrogen Bonding in Water

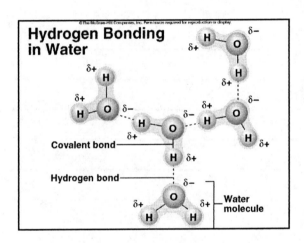

Covalent bond

Hydrogen bond

Water molecule

Percentage and Molar Concentration

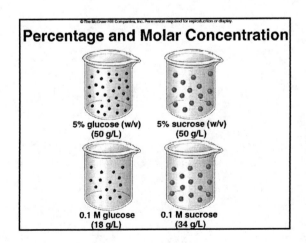

5% glucose (w/v)
(50 g/L)

5% sucrose (w/v)
(50 g/L)

0.1 M glucose
(18 g/L)

0.1 M sucrose
(34 g/L)

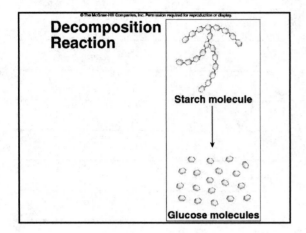

Decomposition Reaction

© The McGraw-Hill Companies, Inc. Permission required for reproduction or display.

Starch molecule

Glucose molecules

_____

_____

_____

_____

_____

_____

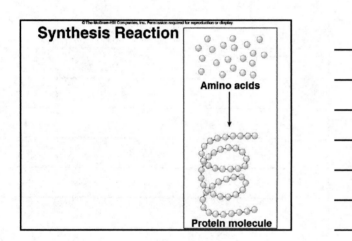

Synthesis Reaction

© The McGraw-Hill Companies, Inc. Permission required for reproduction or display.

Amino acids

Protein molecule

_____

_____

_____

_____

_____

_____

_____

Chapter 3

Anatomy and Physiology: The Unity of Form and Function
Second Edition

Kenneth S. Saladin

Hydration Spheres

Na⁺

Cl⁻

$\delta-$ Oxygen

$\delta+$ $\delta+$

105° Hydrogen

Functional Groups, Organic Molecules

Name and Symbol	Structure	Occurs in
Hydroxyl (—OH)		Sugars, alcohols
Methyl (—CH₃)		Fats, oils, steroids, amino acids
Carboxyl (—COOH)		Amino acids, sugars, proteins
Amino (—NH₂)		Amino acids, proteins
Phosphate (—H₂PO₄)		Nucleic acids, ATP

Synthesis and Hydrolysis Reactions

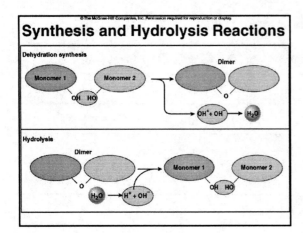

Three Major Monosaccharides

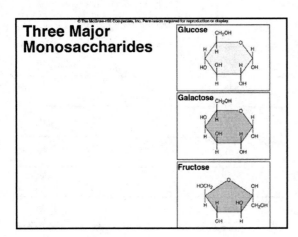

Three Major Disaccharides

Dehydration Synthesis of Maltose

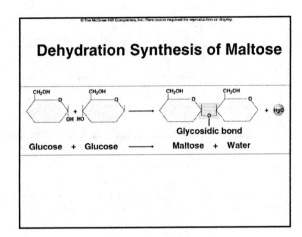

Glycosidic bond

Glucose + Glucose ⟶ Maltose + Water

Maltose Production by Starch Hydrolysis

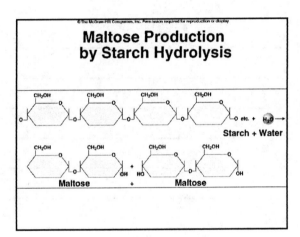

Starch + Water

Maltose + Maltose

Three Major Polysaccharides

Starch (amylose)

Cellulose

Glycogen

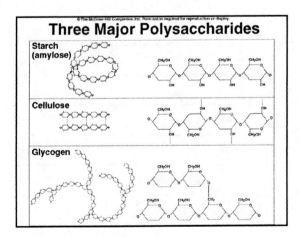

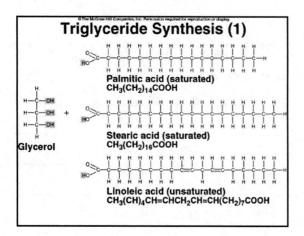

Triglyceride Synthesis (1)

Palmitic acid (saturated)
$CH_3(CH_2)_{14}COOH$

Stearic acid (saturated)
$CH_3(CH_2)_{16}COOH$

Glycerol

Linoleic acid (unsaturated)
$CH_3(CH)_4CH=CHCH_2CH=CH(CH_2)_7COOH$

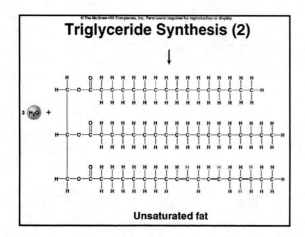

Triglyceride Synthesis (2)

$3\ H_2O$ +

Unsaturated fat

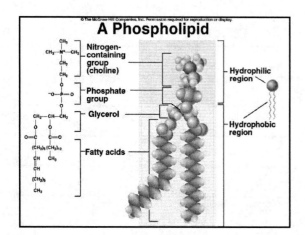

A Phospholipid

Nitrogen-containing group (choline)

Phosphate group

Glycerol

Fatty acids

Hydrophilic region

Hydrophobic region

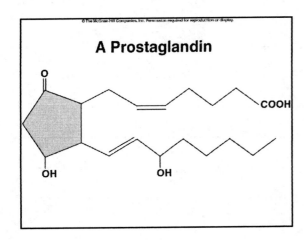

A Prostaglandin

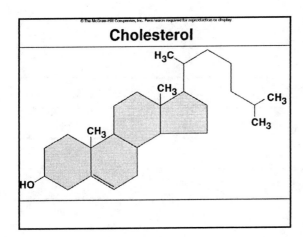

Cholesterol

Amino Acid Structure

Some nonpolar amino acids | Some polar amino acids

Methionine

Cysteine

Amino group

Carboxyl group

Tyrosine

Arginine

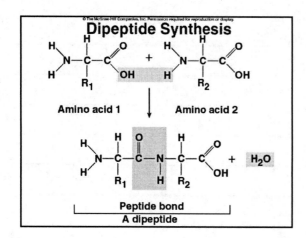

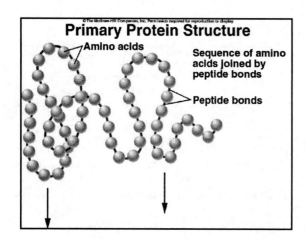

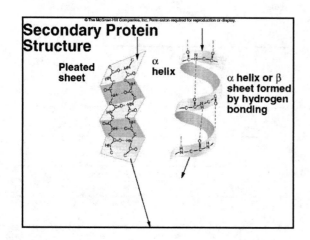

14

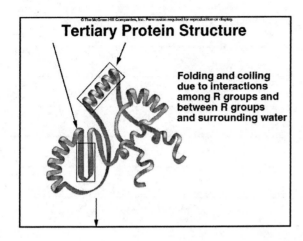

Tertiary Protein Structure

Folding and coiling due to interactions among R groups and between R groups and surrounding water

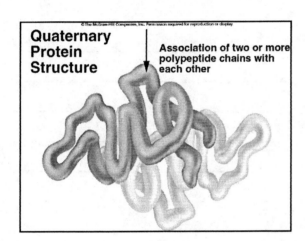

Quaternary Protein Structure

Association of two or more polypeptide chains with each other

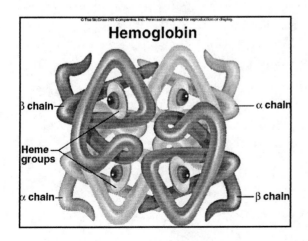

Hemoglobin

β chain

α chain

Heme groups

α chain

β chain

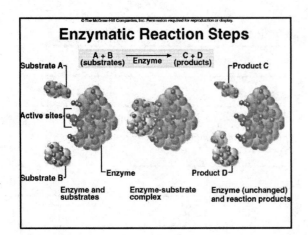

Enzymatic Reaction Steps

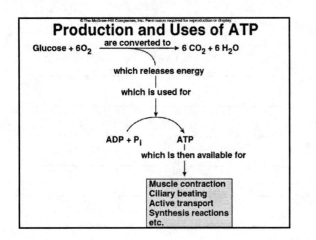

Production and Uses of ATP

Chapter 4

Anatomy and Physiology: The Unity of Form and Function
Second Edition

Kenneth S. Saladin

Cell Shapes (1)

Squamous

Spheroid

Polygonal

Discoid

Cell Shapes (2)

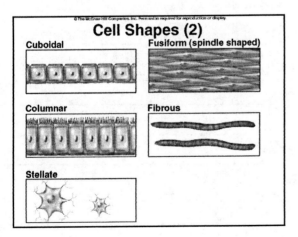

Cuboidal

Fusiform (spindle shaped)

Columnar

Fibrous

Stellate

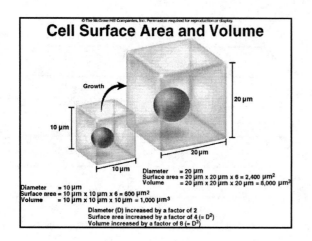

Cell Surface Area and Volume

Growth

20 μm

10 μm

20 μm

10 μm

10 μm

Diameter = 10 μm
Surface area = 10 μm x 10 μm x 6 = 600 μm²
Volume = 10 μm x 10 μm x 10 μm = 1,000 μm³

Diameter = 20 μm
Surface area = 20 μm x 20 μm x 6 = 2,400 μm²
Volume = 20 μm x 20 μm x 20 μm = 8,000 μm³

Diameter (D) increased by a factor of 2
Surface area increased by a factor of 4 (= D²)
Volume increased by a factor of 8 (= D³)

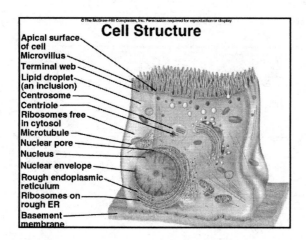

Cell Structure

Apical surface of cell
Microvillus
Terminal web
Lipid droplet (an inclusion)
Centrosome
Centriole
Ribosomes free in cytosol
Microtubule
Nuclear pore
Nucleus
Nuclear envelope
Rough endoplasmic reticulum
Ribosomes on rough ER
Basement membrane

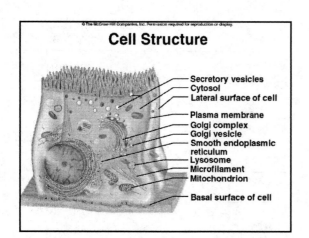

Cell Structure

Secretory vesicles
Cytosol
Lateral surface of cell
Plasma membrane
Golgi complex
Golgi vesicle
Smooth endoplasmic reticulum
Lysosome
Microfilament
Mitochondrion
Basal surface of cell

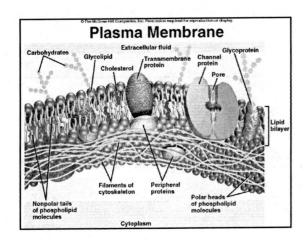

Plasma Membrane

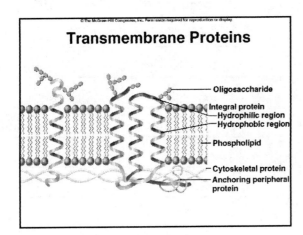

Transmembrane Proteins

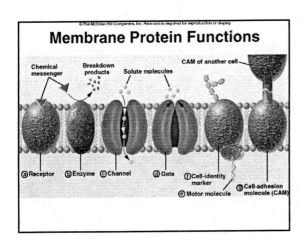

Membrane Protein Functions

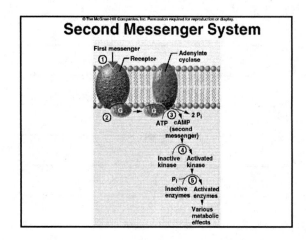

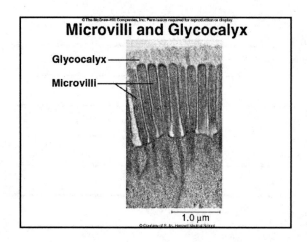

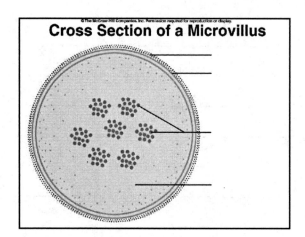

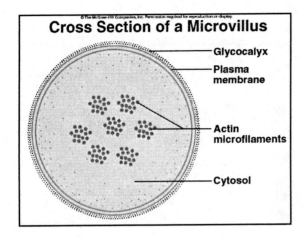

Cross Section of a Microvillus

- Glycocalyx
- Plasma membrane
- Actin microfilaments
- Cytosol

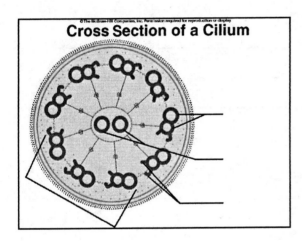

Cross Section of a Cilium

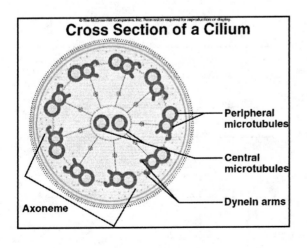

Cross Section of a Cilium

- Peripheral microtubules
- Central microtubules
- Dynein arms

Axoneme

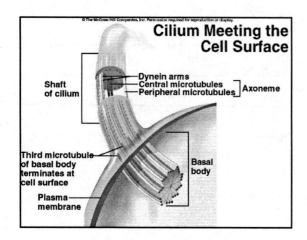

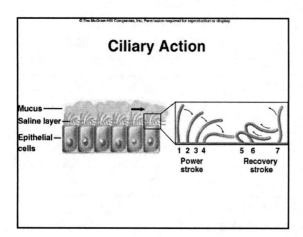

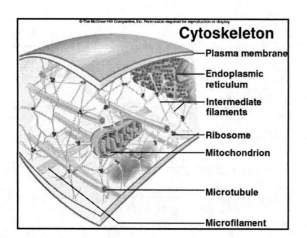

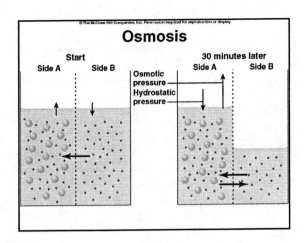

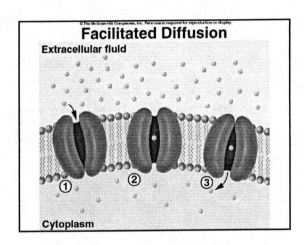

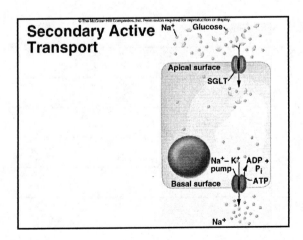

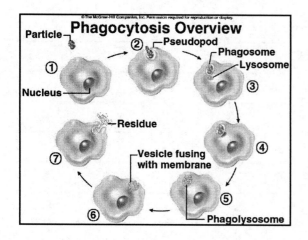

Phagocytosis Overview

- Particle
- Pseudopod
- Phagosome
- Lysosome
- Nucleus
- Residue
- Vesicle fusing with membrane
- Phagolysosome

① ② ③ ④ ⑤ ⑥ ⑦

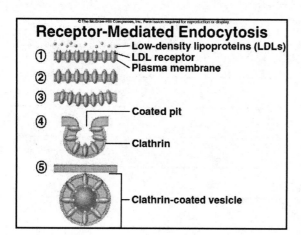

Receptor-Mediated Endocytosis

- Low-density lipoproteins (LDLs)
- LDL receptor
- Plasma membrane
- Coated pit
- Clathrin
- Clathrin-coated vesicle

① ② ③ ④ ⑤

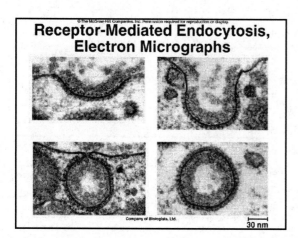

Receptor-Mediated Endocytosis, Electron Micrographs

30 nm

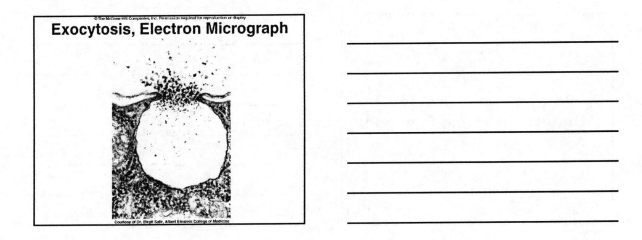

Exocytosis, Electron Micrograph

Courtesy of Dr. Birgit Satir, Albert Einstein College of Medicine

© The McGraw-Hill Companies, Inc. Permission required for reproduction or display.

Chapter 5

Anatomy and Physiology: The Unity of Form and Function
Second Edition

Kenneth S. Saladin

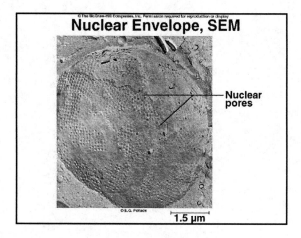

Nuclear Envelope, SEM

Nuclear pores

1.5 μm

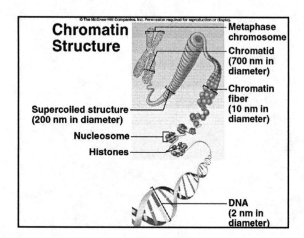

Chromatin Structure

Metaphase chromosome

Chromatid (700 nm in diameter)

Chromatin fiber (10 nm in diameter)

Supercoiled structure (200 nm in diameter)

Nucleosome

Histones

DNA (2 nm in diameter)

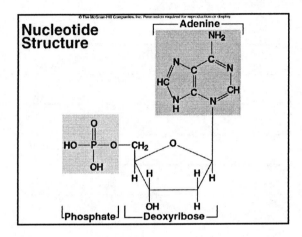

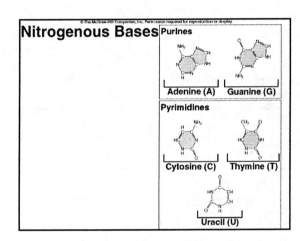

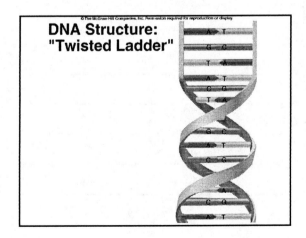

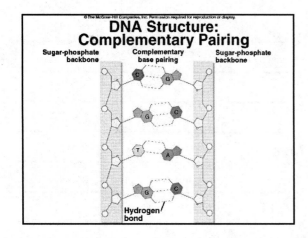

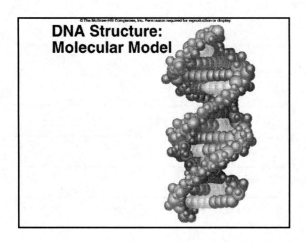

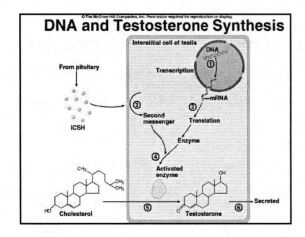

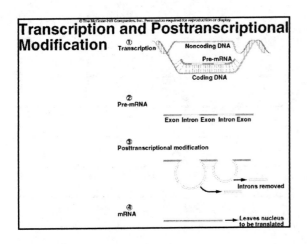

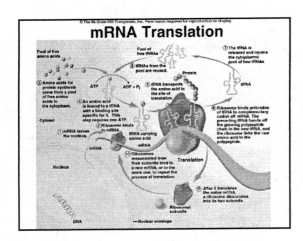

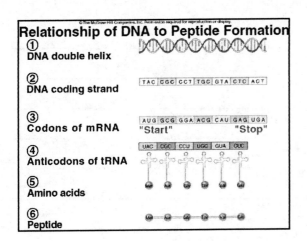

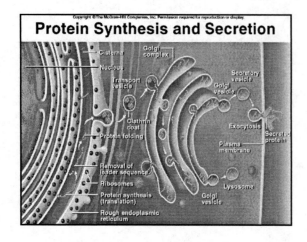

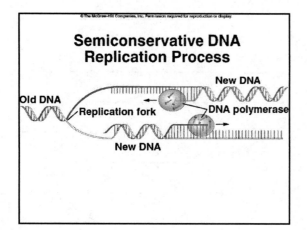

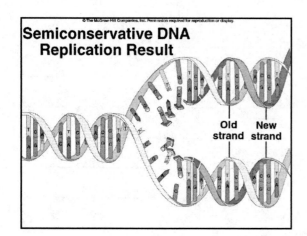

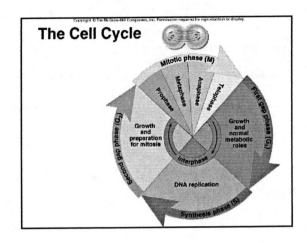

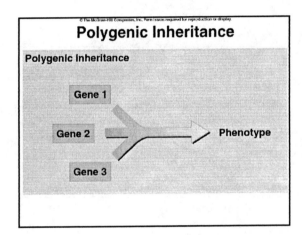

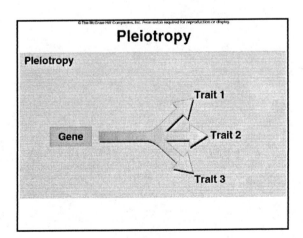

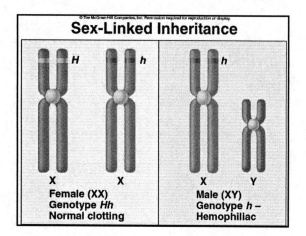

Sex-Linked Inheritance

H   *h*   *h*

X   X   X   Y

Female (XX)
Genotype *Hh*
Normal clotting

Male (XY)
Genotype *h* –
Hemophiliac

_____

_____

_____

_____

_____

_____

_____

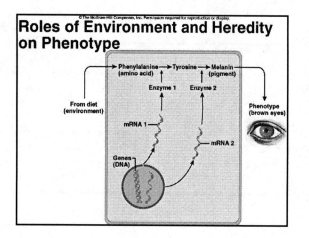

Roles of Environment and Heredity on Phenotype

Phenylalanine → Tyrosine → Melanin
(amino acid)   (pigment)

Enzyme 1   Enzyme 2

From diet
(environment)

Phenotype
(brown eyes)

mRNA 1

mRNA 2

Genes
(DNA)

_____

_____

_____

_____

_____

_____

_____

Chapter 6

Anatomy and Physiology: The Unity of Form and Function
Second Edition

Kenneth S. Saladin

Simple Squamous Epithelium (1)

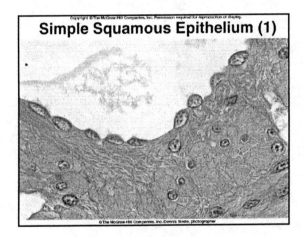

Simple Squamous Epithelium (2)

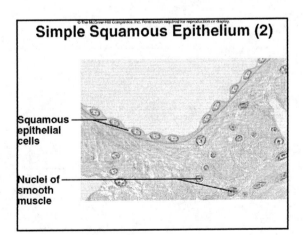

Squamous epithelial cells

Nuclei of smooth muscle

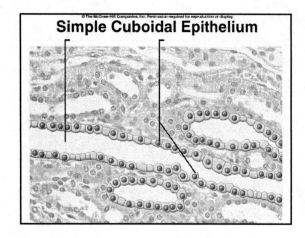

Simple Cuboidal Epithelium

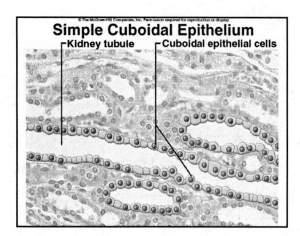

Simple Cuboidal Epithelium
Kidney tubule — Cuboidal epithelial cells

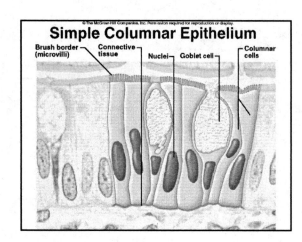

Simple Columnar Epithelium
Brush border (microvilli) — Connective tissue — Nuclei — Goblet cell — Columnar cells

34

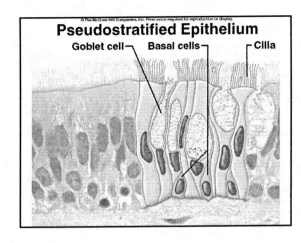

Pseudostratified Epithelium

Goblet cell ⌐ Basal cells ⌐ ⌐ Cilia

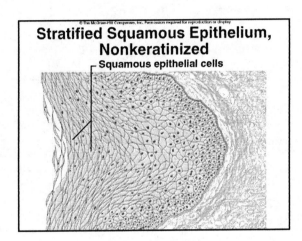

Stratified Squamous Epithelium, Nonkeratinized

⌐ Squamous epithelial cells

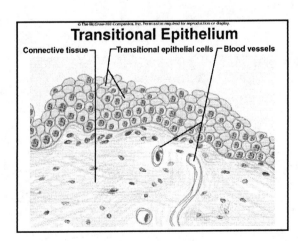

Transitional Epithelium

Connective tissue ⌐   ⌐ Transitional epithelial cells   ⌐ Blood vessels

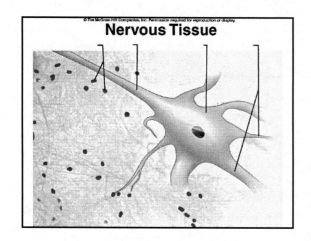

Nervous Tissue

_____

_____

_____

_____

_____

_____

_____

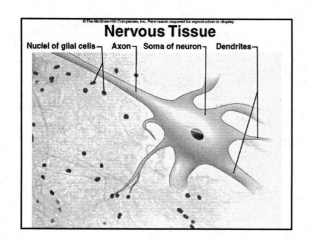

Nervous Tissue

Nuclei of glial cells   Axon   Soma of neuron   Dendrites

_____

_____

_____

_____

_____

_____

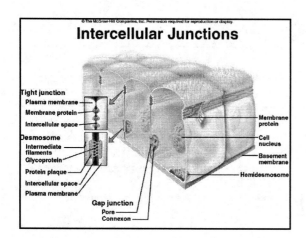

Intercellular Junctions

_____

_____

_____

_____

_____

_____

_____

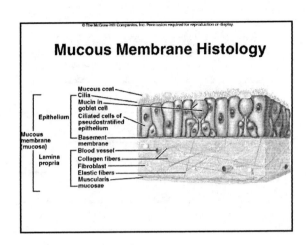

Mucous Membrane Histology

Epithelium
Mucous coat
Cilia
Mucin in goblet cell
Ciliated cells of pseudostratified epithelium
Basement membrane
Mucous membrane (mucosa)
Blood vessel
Lamina propria
Collagen fibers
Fibroblast
Elastic fibers
Muscularis mucosae

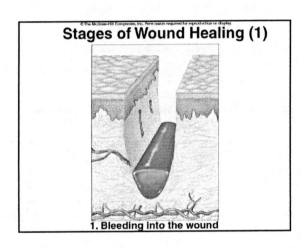

Stages of Wound Healing (1)

1. Bleeding into the wound

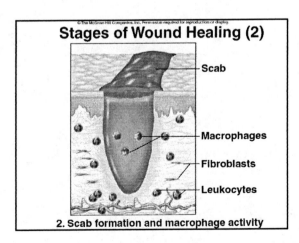

Stages of Wound Healing (2)

Scab
Macrophages
Fibroblasts
Leukocytes

2. Scab formation and macrophage activity

Stages of Wound Healing (3)

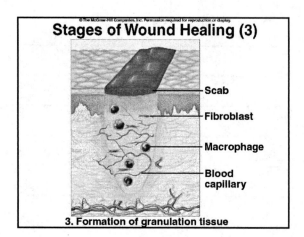

- Scab
- Fibroblast
- Macrophage
- Blood capillary

3. Formation of granulation tissue

_____

_____

_____

_____

_____

_____

_____

Stages of Wound Healing (4)

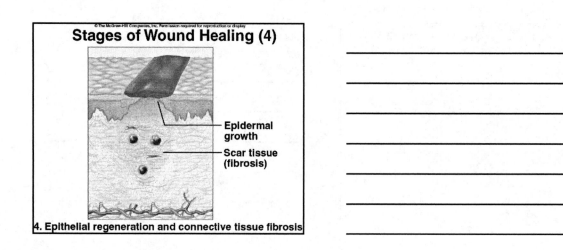

- Epidermal growth
- Scar tissue (fibrosis)

4. Epithelial regeneration and connective tissue fibrosis

_____

_____

_____

_____

_____

_____

_____

Chapter 7

Anatomy and Physiology: The Unity of Form and Function
Second Edition

Kenneth S. Saladin

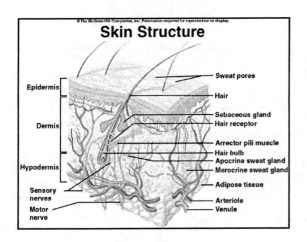

Skin Structure

- Epidermis
- Dermis
- Hypodermis
- Sensory nerves
- Motor nerve
- Sweat pores
- Hair
- Sebaceous gland
- Hair receptor
- Arrector pili muscle
- Hair bulb
- Apocrine sweat gland
- Merocrine sweat gland
- Adipose tissue
- Arteriole
- Venule

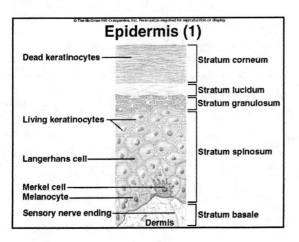

Epidermis (1)

- Dead keratinocytes — Stratum corneum
- Stratum lucidum
- Stratum granulosum
- Living keratinocytes
- Langerhans cell — Stratum spinosum
- Merkel cell
- Melanocyte
- Sensory nerve ending — Stratum basale
- Dermis

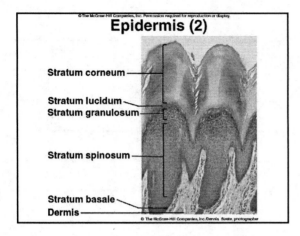

Epidermis (2)

Stratum corneum

Stratum lucidum
Stratum granulosum

Stratum spinosum

Stratum basale
Dermis

© The McGraw-Hill Companies, Inc./Dennis Strete, photographer

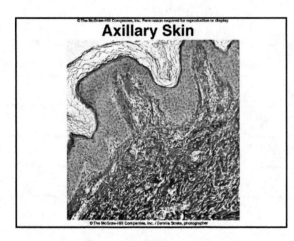

Axillary Skin

©The McGraw-Hill Companies, Inc. /Dennis Strete, photographer

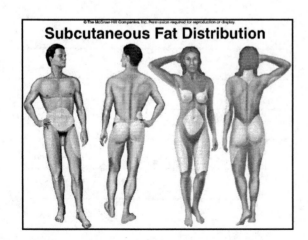

Subcutaneous Fat Distribution

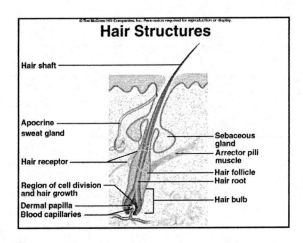

Hair Structures

Hair shaft

Apocrine sweat gland

Hair receptor

Region of cell division and hair growth

Dermal papilla
Blood capillaries

Sebaceous gland
Arrector pili muscle
Hair follicle
Hair root
Hair bulb

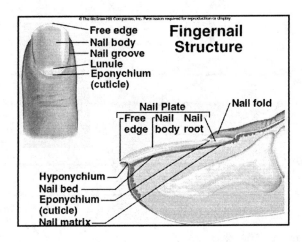

Fingernail Structure

Free edge
Nail body
Nail groove
Lunule
Eponychium (cuticle)

Nail Plate
Free edge | Nail body | Nail root
Nail fold

Hyponychium
Nail bed
Eponychium (cuticle)
Nail matrix

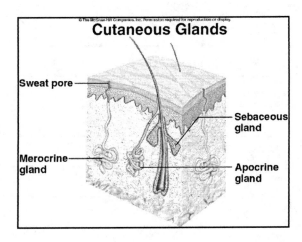

Cutaneous Glands

Sweat pore

Merocrine gland

Sebaceous gland

Apocrine gland

41

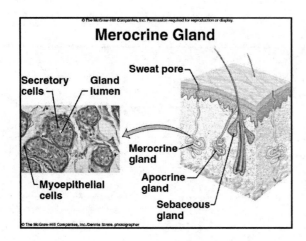

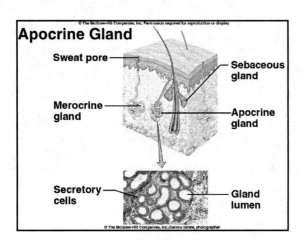

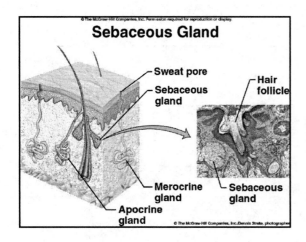

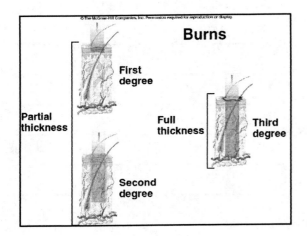

Chapter 8

Anatomy and Physiology: The Unity of Form and Function
Second Edition

Kenneth S. Saladin

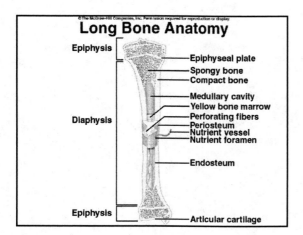

Long Bone Anatomy

- Epiphysis
- Epiphyseal plate
- Spongy bone
- Compact bone
- Medullary cavity
- Yellow bone marrow
- Perforating fibers
- Periosteum
- Nutrient vessel
- Nutrient foramen
- Diaphysis
- Endosteum
- Epiphysis
- Articular cartilage

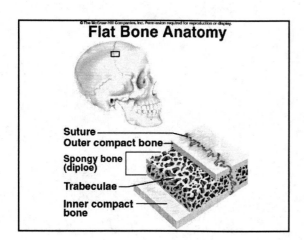

Flat Bone Anatomy

- Suture
- Outer compact bone
- Spongy bone (diploe)
- Trabeculae
- Inner compact bone

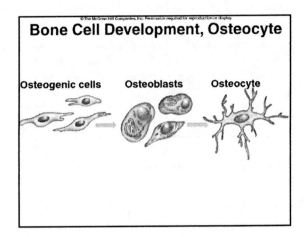

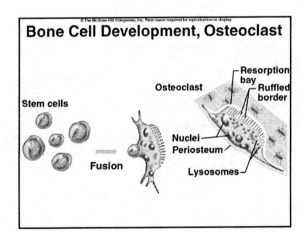

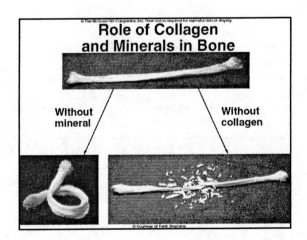

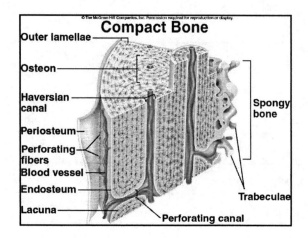

Compact Bone

Outer lamellae
Osteon
Haversian canal
Periosteum
Perforating fibers
Blood vessel
Endosteum
Lacuna
Perforating canal
Spongy bone
Trabeculae

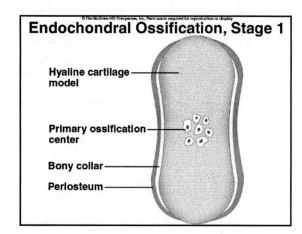

Endochondral Ossification, Stage 1

Hyaline cartilage model
Primary ossification center
Bony collar
Periosteum

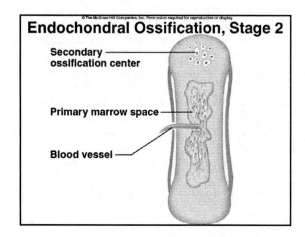

Endochondral Ossification, Stage 2

Secondary ossification center
Primary marrow space
Blood vessel

Endochondral Ossification, Stage 3

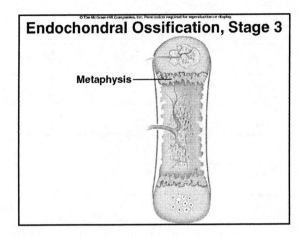

Metaphysis

Endochondral Ossification, Stage 4

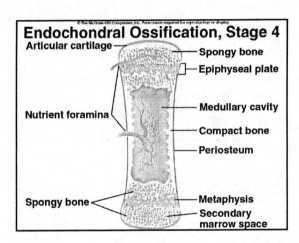

Articular cartilage — Spongy bone

— Epiphyseal plate

Nutrient foramina — Medullary cavity

— Compact bone

— Periosteum

Spongy bone — Metaphysis

Secondary marrow space

Calcitriol Synthesis and Action

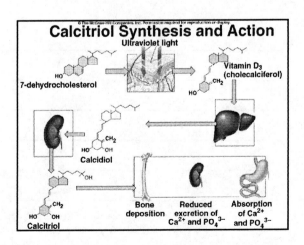

Ultraviolet light

7-dehydrocholesterol

Vitamin D_3 (cholecalciferol)

CH_2

CH_2

HO OH
Calcidiol

CH_2

HO OH
Calcitriol

Bone deposition

Reduced excretion of Ca^{2+} and PO_4^{3-}

Absorption of Ca^{2+} and PO_4^{3-}

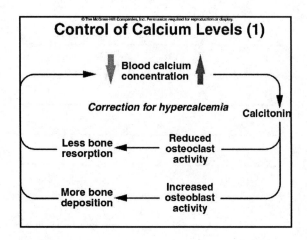

Control of Calcium Levels (1)

Correction for hypercalcemia

Blood calcium concentration ↓ ↑

Calcitonin

Reduced osteoclast activity → Less bone resorption

Increased osteoblast activity → More bone deposition

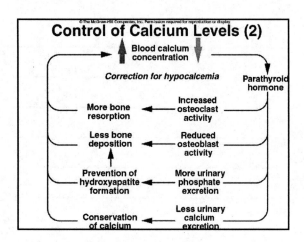

Control of Calcium Levels (2)

Blood calcium concentration ↑ ↓

Correction for hypocalcemia

Parathyroid hormone

Increased osteoclast activity → More bone resorption

Reduced osteoblast activity → Less bone deposition

More urinary phosphate excretion → Prevention of hydroxyapatite formation

Less urinary calcium excretion → Conservation of calcium

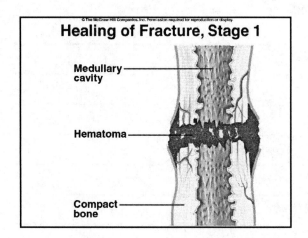

Healing of Fracture, Stage 1

Medullary cavity

Hematoma

Compact bone

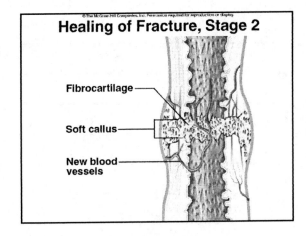

Healing of Fracture, Stage 2

Fibrocartilage
Soft callus
New blood vessels

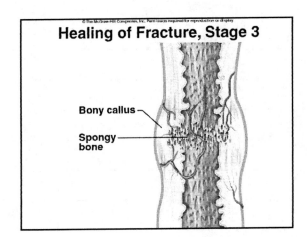

Healing of Fracture, Stage 3

Bony callus
Spongy bone

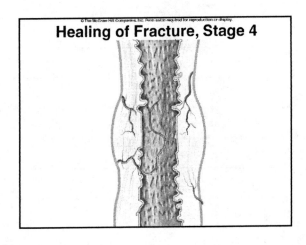

Healing of Fracture, Stage 4

Chapter 9

Anatomy and Physiology: The Unity of Form and Function
Second Edition

Kenneth S. Saladin

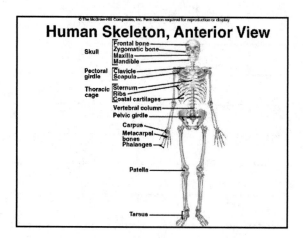

Human Skeleton, Anterior View

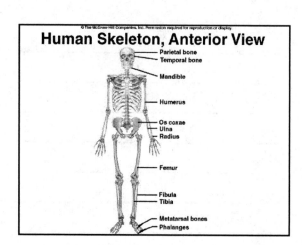

Human Skeleton, Anterior View

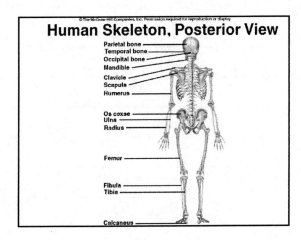

Human Skeleton, Posterior View

Parietal bone
Temporal bone
Occipital bone
Mandible
Clavicle
Scapula
Humerus
Os coxae
Ulna
Radius
Femur
Fibula
Tibia
Calcaneus

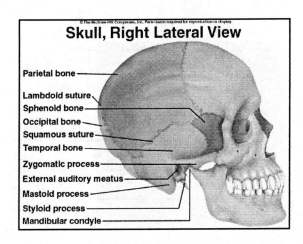

Skull, Right Lateral View

Parietal bone
Lambdoid suture
Sphenoid bone
Occipital bone
Squamous suture
Temporal bone
Zygomatic process
External auditory meatus
Mastoid process
Styloid process
Mandibular condyle

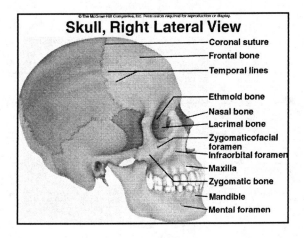

Skull, Right Lateral View

Coronal suture
Frontal bone
Temporal lines
Ethmoid bone
Nasal bone
Lacrimal bone
Zygomaticofacial foramen
Infraorbital foramen
Maxilla
Zygomatic bone
Mandible
Mental foramen

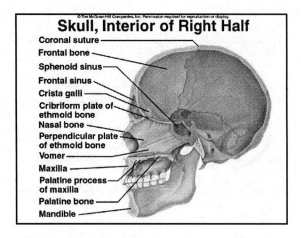

Skull, Interior of Right Half

- Coronal suture
- Frontal bone
- Sphenoid sinus
- Frontal sinus
- Crista galli
- Cribriform plate of ethmoid bone
- Nasal bone
- Perpendicular plate of ethmoid bone
- Vomer
- Maxilla
- Palatine process of maxilla
- Palatine bone
- Mandible

_____

_____

_____

_____

_____

_____

_____

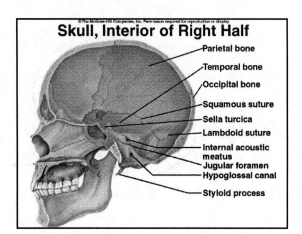

Skull, Interior of Right Half

- Parietal bone
- Temporal bone
- Occipital bone
- Squamous suture
- Sella turcica
- Lambdoid suture
- Internal acoustic meatus
- Jugular foramen
- Hypoglossal canal
- Styloid process

_____

_____

_____

_____

_____

_____

_____

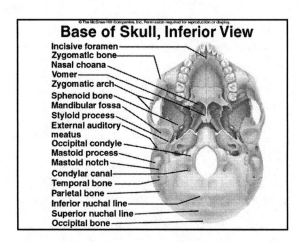

Base of Skull, Inferior View

- Incisive foramen
- Zygomatic bone
- Nasal choana
- Vomer
- Zygomatic arch
- Sphenoid bone
- Mandibular fossa
- Styloid process
- External auditory meatus
- Occipital condyle
- Mastoid process
- Mastoid notch
- Condylar canal
- Temporal bone
- Parietal bone
- Inferior nuchal line
- Superior nuchal line
- Occipital bone

_____

_____

_____

_____

_____

_____

_____

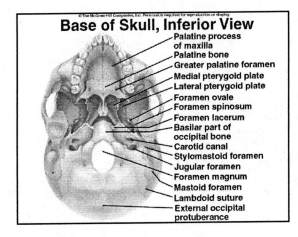

Base of Skull, Inferior View

- Palatine process of maxilla
- Palatine bone
- Greater palatine foramen
- Medial pterygoid plate
- Lateral pterygoid plate
- Foramen ovale
- Foramen spinosum
- Foramen lacerum
- Basilar part of occipital bone
- Carotid canal
- Stylomastoid foramen
- Jugular foramen
- Foramen magnum
- Mastoid foramen
- Lambdoid suture
- External occipital protuberance

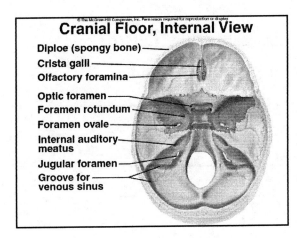

Cranial Floor, Internal View

- Diploe (spongy bone)
- Crista galli
- Olfactory foramina
- Optic foramen
- Foramen rotundum
- Foramen ovale
- Internal auditory meatus
- Jugular foramen
- Groove for venous sinus

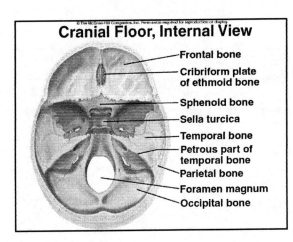

Cranial Floor, Internal View

- Frontal bone
- Cribriform plate of ethmoid bone
- Sphenoid bone
- Sella turcica
- Temporal bone
- Petrous part of temporal bone
- Parietal bone
- Foramen magnum
- Occipital bone

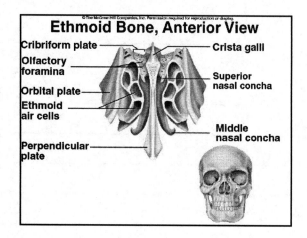

Ethmoid Bone, Anterior View

Cribriform plate — Crista galli
Olfactory foramina
Orbital plate — Superior nasal concha
Ethmoid air cells
Perpendicular plate — Middle nasal concha

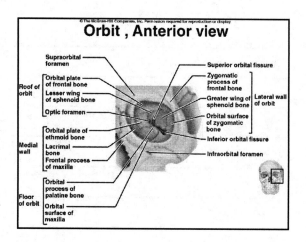

Orbit , Anterior view

Supraorbital foramen — Superior orbital fissure

Roof of orbit
Orbital plate of frontal bone — Zygomatic process of frontal bone
Lesser wing of sphenoid bone — Greater wing of sphenoid bone — Lateral wall of orbit
Optic foramen — Orbital surface of zygomatic bone

Medial wall
Orbital plate of ethmoid bone — Inferior orbital fissure
Lacrimal bone — Infraorbital foramen
Frontal process of maxilla

Floor of orbit
Orbital process of palatine bone
Orbital surface of maxilla

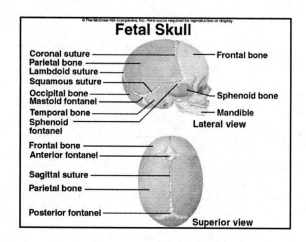

Fetal Skull

Coronal suture — Frontal bone
Parietal bone
Lambdoid suture
Squamous suture
Occipital bone — Sphenoid bone
Mastoid fontanel
Temporal bone — Mandible
Sphenoid fontanel — Lateral view

Frontal bone
Anterior fontanel

Sagittal suture

Parietal bone

Posterior fontanel — Superior view

54

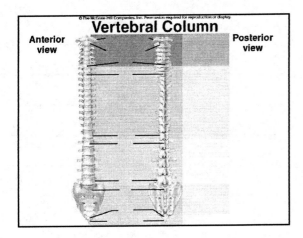

Vertebral Column

Anterior view

Posterior view

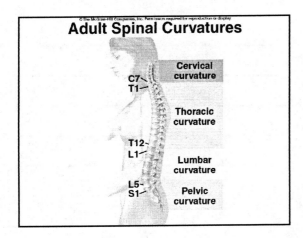

Adult Spinal Curvatures

C7
T1
Cervical curvature

Thoracic curvature

T12
L1
Lumbar curvature

L5
S1
Pelvic curvature

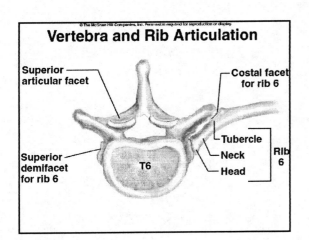

Vertebra and Rib Articulation

Superior articular facet

Costal facet for rib 6

Superior demifacet for rib 6

T6

Tubercle
Neck
Head

Rib 6

Pelvic Girdle

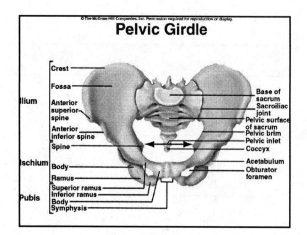

- Ilium
  - Crest
  - Fossa
  - Anterior superior spine
  - Anterior inferior spine
  - Spine
- Ischium
  - Body
  - Ramus
- Pubis
  - Superior ramus
  - Inferior ramus
  - Body
  - Symphysis
- Base of sacrum
- Sacroiliac joint
- Pelvic surface of sacrum
- Pelvic brim
- Pelvic inlet
- Coccyx
- Acetabulum
- Obturator foramen

Os Coxae, Lateral View

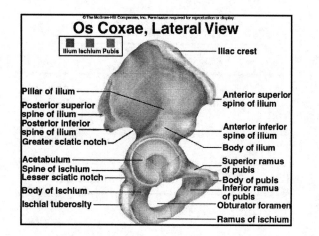

Ilium Ischium Pubis

- Pillar of ilium
- Posterior superior spine of ilium
- Posterior inferior spine of ilium
- Greater sciatic notch
- Acetabulum
- Spine of ischium
- Lesser sciatic notch
- Body of ischium
- Ischial tuberosity
- Iliac crest
- Anterior superior spine of ilium
- Anterior inferior spine of ilium
- Body of ilium
- Superior ramus of pubis
- Body of pubis
- Inferior ramus of pubis
- Obturator foramen
- Ramus of ischium

Chapter 10

Anatomy and Physiology: The Unity of Form and Function
Second Edition

Kenneth S. Saladin

Joint Classification Systems

Structural classification Based on the way bones are held together	Functional classification Based on relative joint mobility
Synovial joints: Bones separated by a joint cavity, lubricated by synovial fluid, enclosed in fibrous joint capsule *Examples:* shoulder, elbow, carpal joints hip, knee, tarsal joints interphalangeal joints joints between articular processes of cervical to lumbar vertebrae	**Diarthroses:** Freely movable synovial joints *Examples:* shoulder, elbow, carpal joints hip, knee, tarsal joints interphalangeal joints
Fibrous joints: Bones held together by collagenous fibers extending from the matrix of one bone into the matrix of the next; no joint cavity *Examples:* skull sutures teeth in sockets distal radioulnar joints tibiofibular joints	**Amphiarthroses:** Slightly movable joints *Examples:* intervertebral discs joints between articular processes of cervical to lumbar vertebrae costosternal joints (ribs 2–7) pubic symphysis distal radioulnar joints tibiofibular joints
Cartilaginous joints: Bones held together by cartilage; no joint cavity *Examples:* epiphyseal plates of long bones costosternal joints pubic symphysis intervertebral discs	**Synarthroses:** Joints with little or no movement *Examples:* skull sutures teeth in sockets epiphyseal plates of long bones first costosternal joint mental symphysis

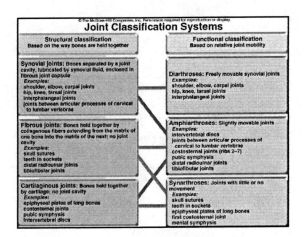

Types of Fibrous Joints

Fibrous connective tissue

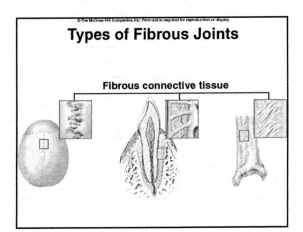

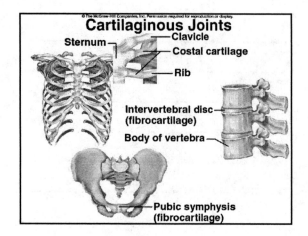

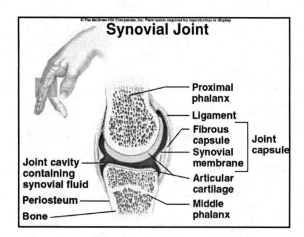

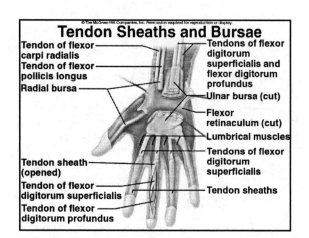

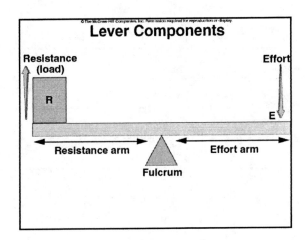

Lever Components

Resistance (load)

R

Effort

E

Resistance arm

Effort arm

Fulcrum

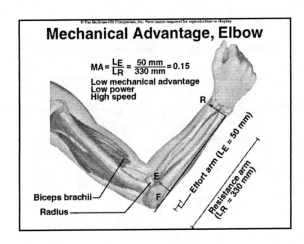

Mechanical Advantage, Elbow

$$MA = \frac{L_E}{L_R} = \frac{50\ mm}{330\ mm} = 0.15$$

Low mechanical advantage
Low power
High speed

R

Effort arm (L_E = 50 mm)

Resistance arm (L_R = 330 mm)

Biceps brachii

Radius

E

F

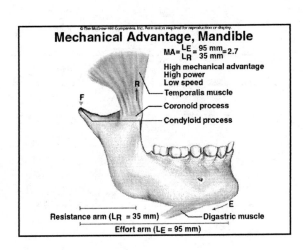

Mechanical Advantage, Mandible

$$MA = \frac{L_E}{L_R} = \frac{95\ mm}{35\ mm} = 2.7$$

High mechanical advantage
High power
Low speed

R

Temporalis muscle

Coronoid process

Condyloid process

F

Resistance arm (L_R = 35 mm)

Effort arm (L_E = 95 mm)

E

Digastric muscle

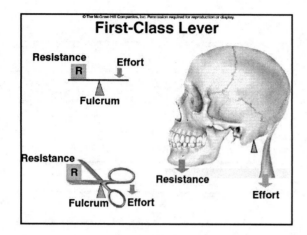

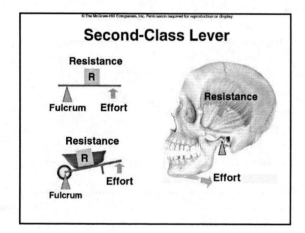

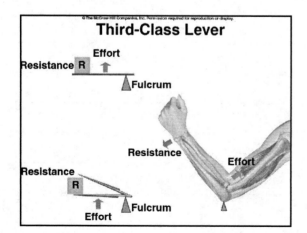

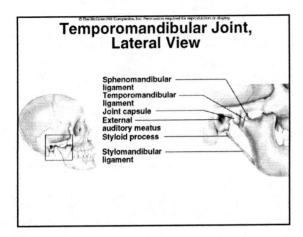

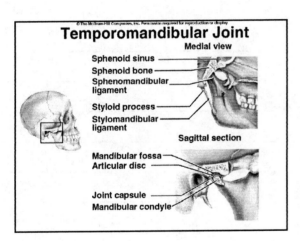

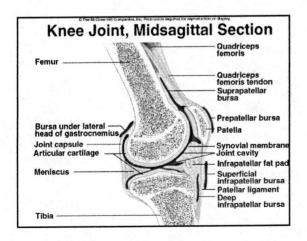

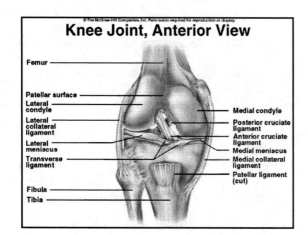

Knee Joint, Anterior View

Femur

Patellar surface

Lateral condyle

Lateral collateral ligament

Lateral meniscus

Transverse ligament

Fibula

Tibia

Medial condyle

Posterior cruciate ligament

Anterior cruciate ligament

Medial meniscus

Medial collateral ligament

Patellar ligament (cut)

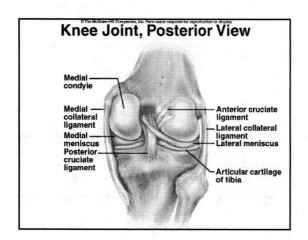

Knee Joint, Posterior View

Medial condyle

Medial collateral ligament

Medial meniscus

Posterior cruciate ligament

Anterior cruciate ligament

Lateral collateral ligament

Lateral meniscus

Articular cartilage of tibia

Chapter 11

Anatomy and Physiology: The Unity of Form and Function

Second Edition

Kenneth S. Saladin

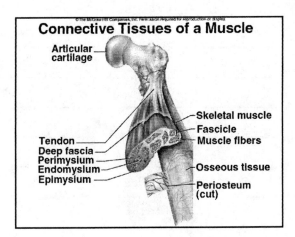

Connective Tissues of a Muscle

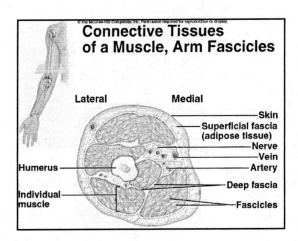

Connective Tissues of a Muscle, Arm Fascicles

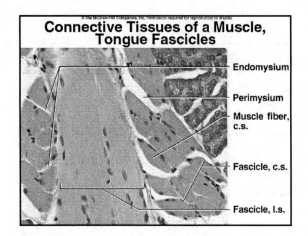

Connective Tissues of a Muscle, Tongue Fascicles

- Endomysium
- Perimysium
- Muscle fiber, c.s.
- Fascicle, c.s.
- Fascicle, l.s.

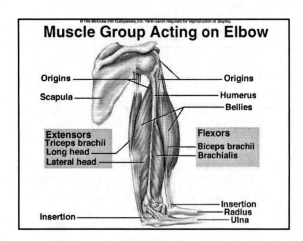

Muscle Group Acting on Elbow

- Origins
- Scapula
- Origins
- Humerus
- Bellies

Extensors
Triceps brachii
Long head
Lateral head

Flexors
Biceps brachii
Brachialis

- Insertion
- Radius
- Ulna
- Insertion

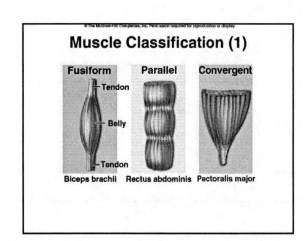

Muscle Classification (1)

Fusiform
- Tendon
- Belly
- Tendon

Biceps brachii

Parallel

Rectus abdominis

Convergent

Pectoralis major

Muscle Classification (2)

Unipennate	Bipennate	Multipennate	Circular
Palmar interosseous	Rectus femoris	Deltoid	Orbicularis oculi

_____

_____

_____

_____

_____

_____

Muscular System, Anterior View

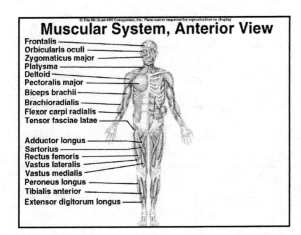

Frontalis
Orbicularis oculi
Zygomaticus major
Platysma
Deltoid
Pectoralis major
Biceps brachii
Brachioradialis
Flexor carpi radialis
Tensor fasciae latae

Adductor longus
Sartorius
Rectus femoris
Vastus lateralis
Vastus medialis
Peroneus longus
Tibialis anterior
Extensor digitorum longus

_____

_____

_____

_____

_____

_____

Muscular System, Anterior View

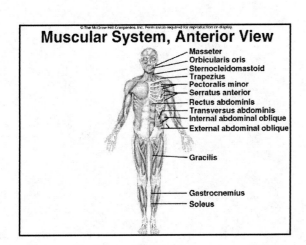

Masseter
Orbicularis oris
Sternocleidomastoid
Trapezius
Pectoralis minor
Serratus anterior
Rectus abdominis
Transversus abdominis
Internal abdominal oblique
External abdominal oblique

Gracilis

Gastrocnemius
Soleus

_____

_____

_____

_____

_____

_____

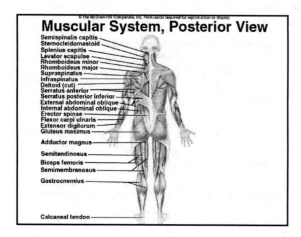

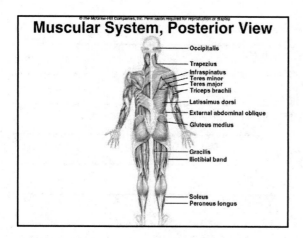

_____

_____

_____

_____

_____

_____

_____

_____

_____

_____

_____

_____

_____

Chapter 12

Anatomy and Physiology: The Unity of Form and Function
Second Edition

Kenneth S. Saladin

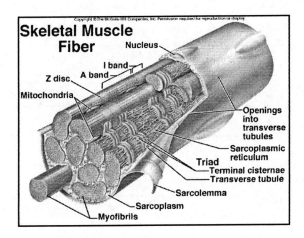

Skeletal Muscle Fiber

Nucleus
I band
A band
Z disc
Mitochondria
Openings into transverse tubules
Sarcoplasmic reticulum
Triad
Terminal cisternae
Transverse tubule
Sarcolemma
Sarcoplasm
Myofibrils

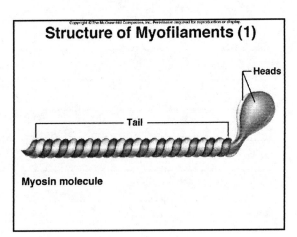

Structure of Myofilaments (1)

Heads
Tail
Myosin molecule

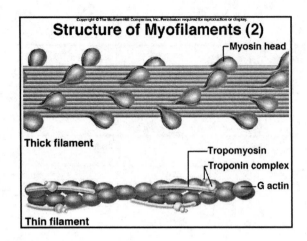

Structure of Myofilaments (2)

Myosin head

Thick filament

Tropomyosin

Troponin complex

G actin

Thin filament

_____

_____

_____

_____

_____

_____

_____

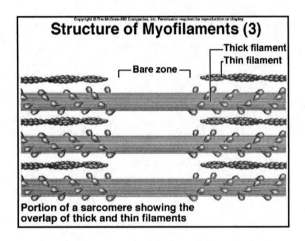

Structure of Myofilaments (3)

Thick filament

Thin filament

Bare zone

Portion of a sarcomere showing the overlap of thick and thin filaments

_____

_____

_____

_____

_____

_____

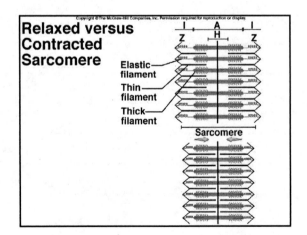

Relaxed versus Contracted Sarcomere

Elastic filament

Thin filament

Thick filament

Sarcomere

_____

_____

_____

_____

_____

_____

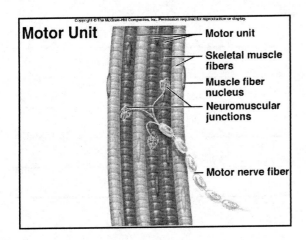

Motor Unit

- Motor unit
- Skeletal muscle fibers
- Muscle fiber nucleus
- Neuromuscular junctions
- Motor nerve fiber

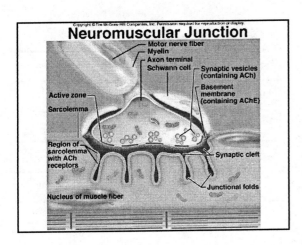

Neuromuscular Junction

- Motor nerve fiber
- Myelin
- Axon terminal
- Schwann cell
- Synaptic vesicles (containing ACh)
- Basement membrane (containing AChE)
- Active zone
- Sarcolemma
- Region of sarcolemma with ACh receptors
- Synaptic cleft
- Nucleus of muscle fiber
- Junctional folds

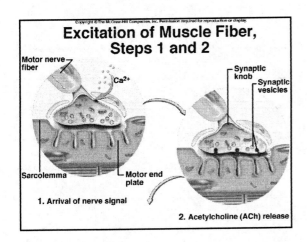

Excitation of Muscle Fiber, Steps 1 and 2

- Motor nerve fiber
- Ca²⁺
- Synaptic knob
- Synaptic vesicles
- Sarcolemma
- Motor end plate
1. Arrival of nerve signal
2. Acetylcholine (ACh) release

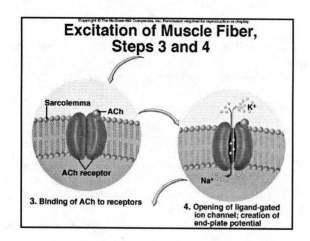

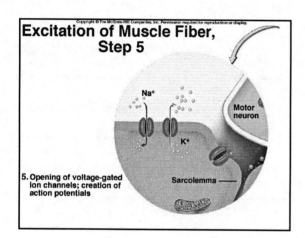

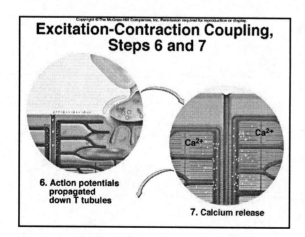

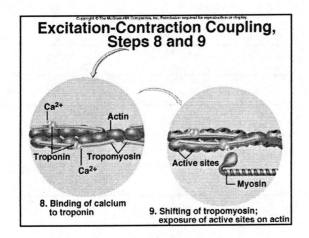

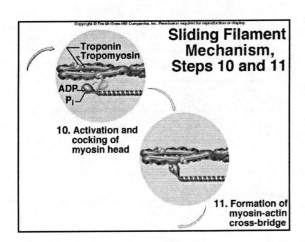

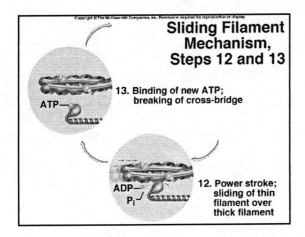

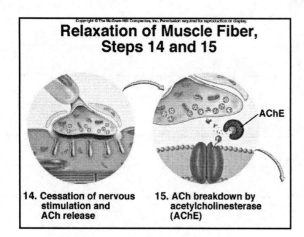

Relaxation of Muscle Fiber, Steps 14 and 15

AChE

14. Cessation of nervous stimulation and ACh release

15. ACh breakdown by acetylcholinesterase (AChE)

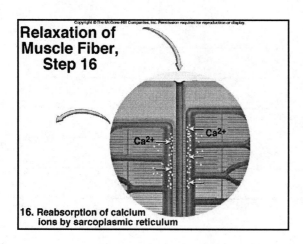

Relaxation of Muscle Fiber, Step 16

Ca^{2+} Ca^{2+}

16. Reabsorption of calcium ions by sarcoplasmic reticulum

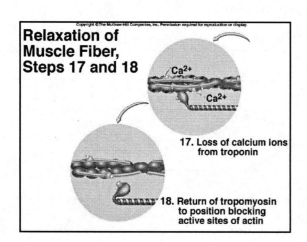

Relaxation of Muscle Fiber, Steps 17 and 18

Ca^{2+}

Ca^{2+}

17. Loss of calcium ions from troponin

18. Return of tropomyosin to position blocking active sites of actin

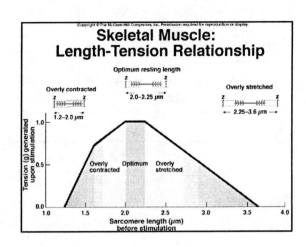

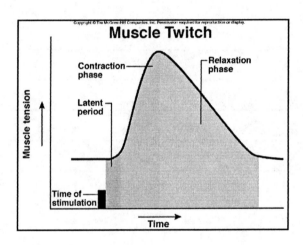

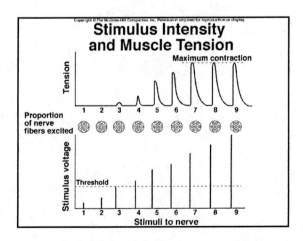

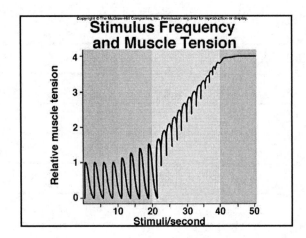

Stimulus Frequency and Muscle Tension

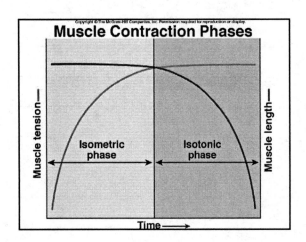

Muscle Contraction Phases

Chapter 13

Anatomy and Physiology: The Unity of Form and Function

Second Edition

Kenneth S. Saladin

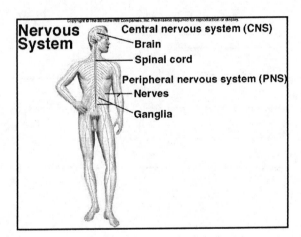

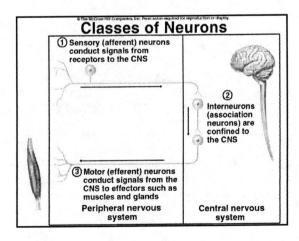

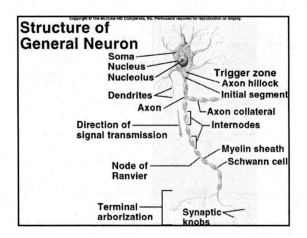

Structure of General Neuron

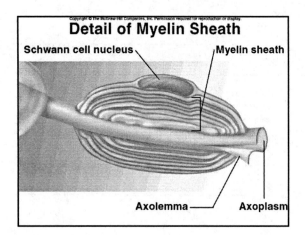

Detail of Myelin Sheath

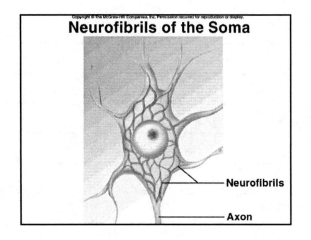

Neurofibrils of the Soma

_____

_____

_____

_____

_____

_____

_____

_____

_____

_____

_____

_____

_____

_____

_____

_____

_____

_____

Nissl Bodies

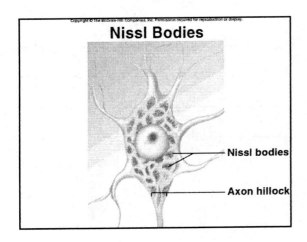

- Nissl bodies
- Axon hillock

Neuronal Structure

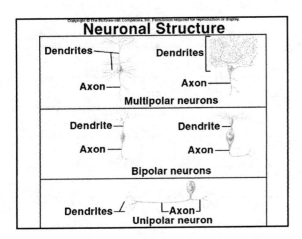

Dendrites —   Dendrites

Axon —   Axon —

Multipolar neurons

Dendrite —   Dendrite —

Axon —   Axon —

Bipolar neurons

Dendrites —   — Axon

Unipolar neuron

Neuroglia of the CNS

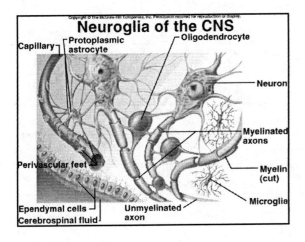

Capillary
Protoplasmic astrocyte
Oligodendrocyte
Neuron
Myelinated axons
Myelin (cut)
Microglia
Perivascular feet
Ependymal cells
Cerebrospinal fluid
Unmyelinated axon

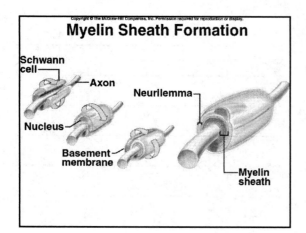

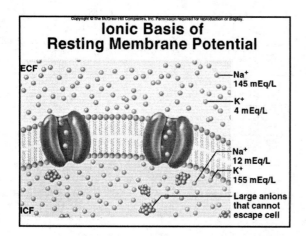

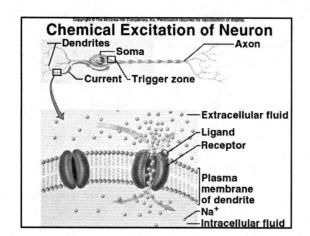

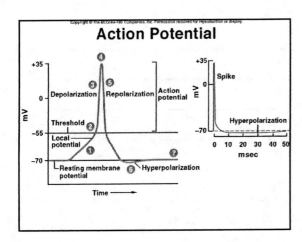

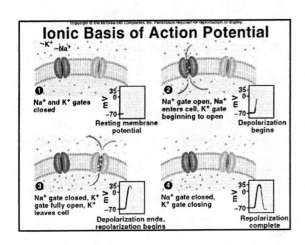

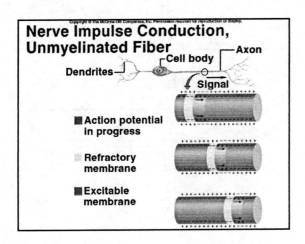

Saltatory Conduction, Myelinated Fiber (1)

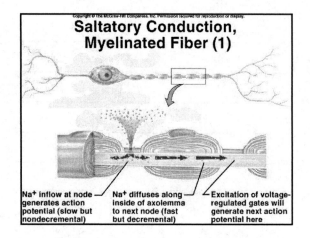

Na⁺ inflow at node generates action potential (slow but nondecremental)

Na⁺ diffuses along inside of axolemma to next node (fast but decremental)

Excitation of voltage-regulated gates will generate next action potential here

Saltatory Conduction, Myelinated Fiber (2)

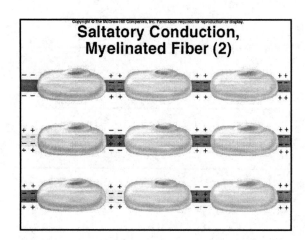

Chemical Synapse Structure

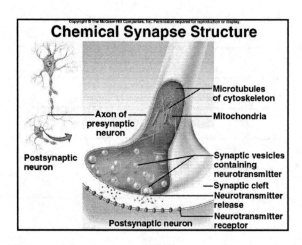

Axon of presynaptic neuron

Postsynaptic neuron

Microtubules of cytoskeleton

Mitochondria

Synaptic vesicles containing neurotransmitter

Synaptic cleft

Neurotransmitter release

Neurotransmitter receptor

Postsynaptic neuron

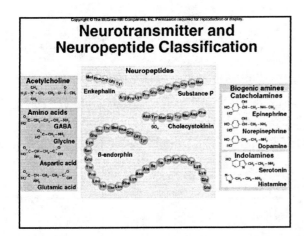

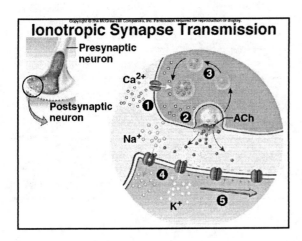

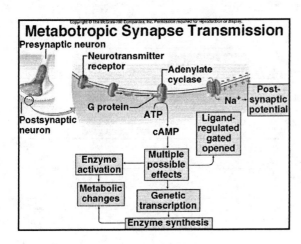

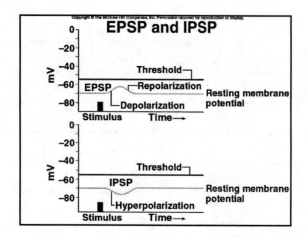

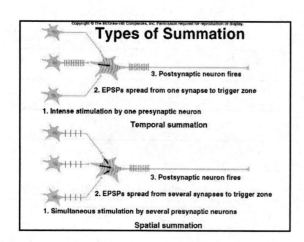

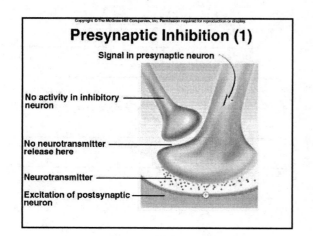

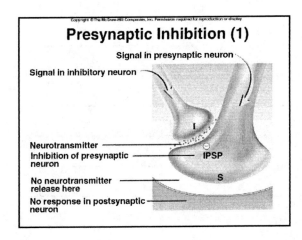

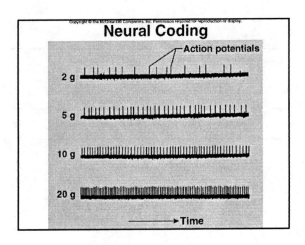

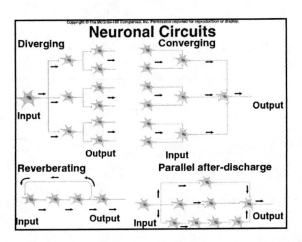

Chapter 14

Anatomy and Physiology: The Unity of Form and Function
Second Edition

Kenneth S. Saladin

Brain, Superior View

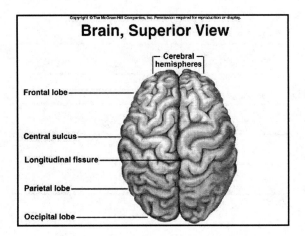

- Cerebral hemispheres
- Frontal lobe
- Central sulcus
- Longitudinal fissure
- Parietal lobe
- Occipital lobe

Brain, Inferior View

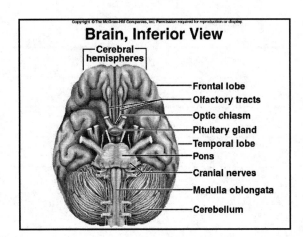

- Cerebral hemispheres
- Frontal lobe
- Olfactory tracts
- Optic chiasm
- Pituitary gland
- Temporal lobe
- Pons
- Cranial nerves
- Medulla oblongata
- Cerebellum

Brain, Lateral View

Rostral ◄──── ────► Caudal

Central sulcus

Gyrus

Lateral fissure

Cerebrum

Temporal lobe

Brainstem

Cerebellum

Spinal cord

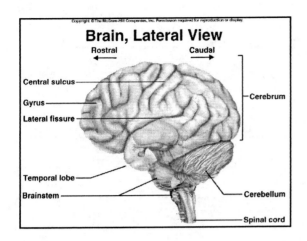

Brain, Midsagittal Section

Frontal lobe

Corpus callosum

Thalamus

Hypothalamus

Midbrain

Pons

Medulla oblongata

Spinal cord

Central sulcus

Parietal lobe

Parieto-occipital sulcus

Occipital lobe

Cerebellum

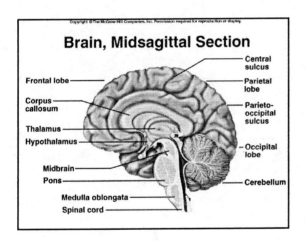

Meninges of Head

Dura mater

Periosteal layer

Meningeal layer

Subdural space

Arachnoid mater

Subarachnoid space

Pia mater

Blood vessel

Falx cerebri (in longitudinal fissure only)

Skull

Arachnoid villus

Superior sagittal sinus

Gray matter

White matter

Brain

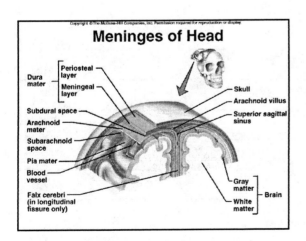

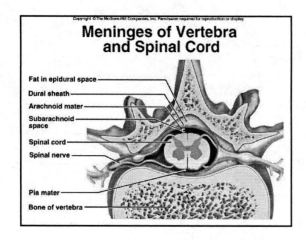

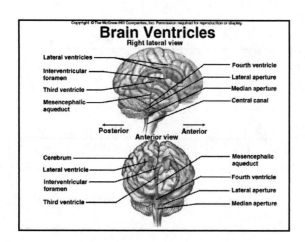

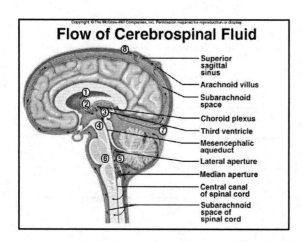

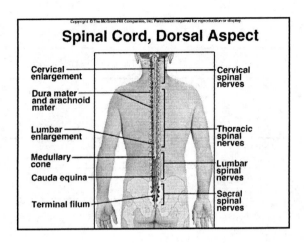

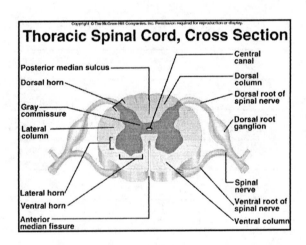

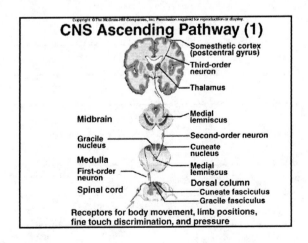

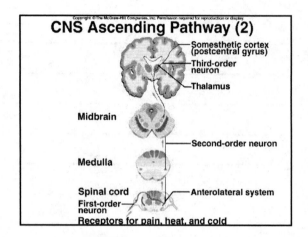

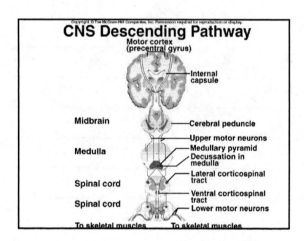

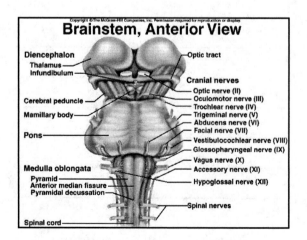

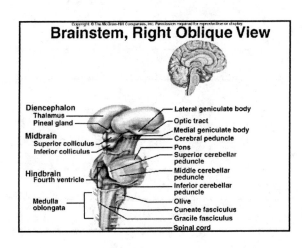

Brainstem, Right Oblique View

Diencephalon
Thalamus
Pineal gland

Midbrain
Superior colliculus
Inferior colliculus

Hindbrain
Fourth ventricle

Medulla
oblongata

Lateral geniculate body
Optic tract
Medial geniculate body
Cerebral peduncle
Pons
Superior cerebellar peduncle
Middle cerebellar peduncle
Inferior cerebellar peduncle
Olive
Cuneate fasciculus
Gracile fasciculus
Spinal cord

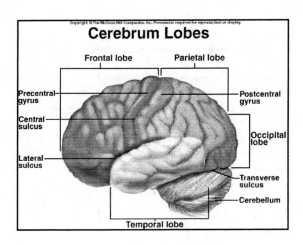

Cerebrum Lobes

Frontal lobe
Parietal lobe
Precentral gyrus
Postcentral gyrus
Central sulcus
Occipital lobe
Lateral sulcus
Transverse sulcus
Cerebellum
Temporal lobe

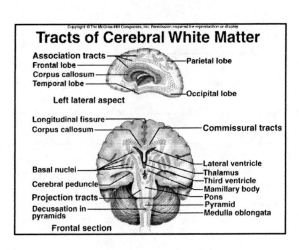

Tracts of Cerebral White Matter

Association tracts
Frontal lobe
Corpus callosum
Temporal lobe
Parietal lobe
Occipital lobe

Left lateral aspect

Longitudinal fissure
Corpus callosum
Commissural tracts
Basal nuclei
Lateral ventricle
Thalamus
Third ventricle
Cerebral peduncle
Mamillary body
Projection tracts
Pons
Pyramid
Decussation in pyramids
Medulla oblongata

Frontal section

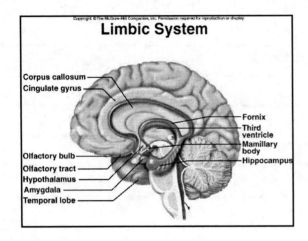

Limbic System

Corpus callosum
Cingulate gyrus
Fornix
Third ventricle
Mamillary body
Olfactory bulb
Olfactory tract
Hypothalamus
Amygdala
Temporal lobe
Hippocampus

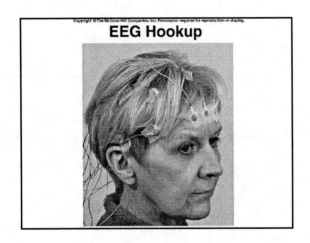

EEG Hookup

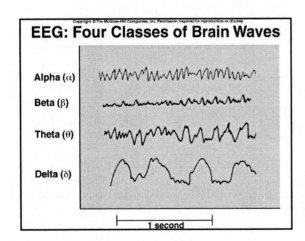

EEG: Four Classes of Brain Waves

Alpha (α)
Beta (β)
Theta (θ)
Delta (δ)

1 second

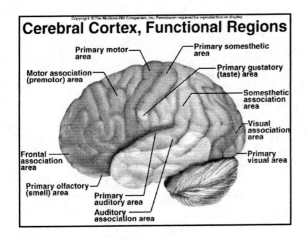

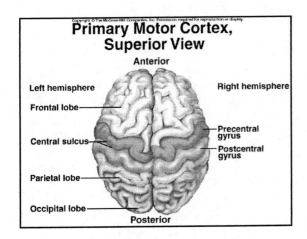

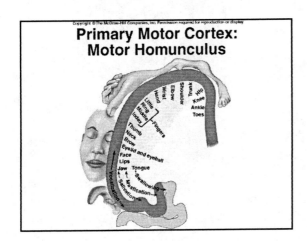

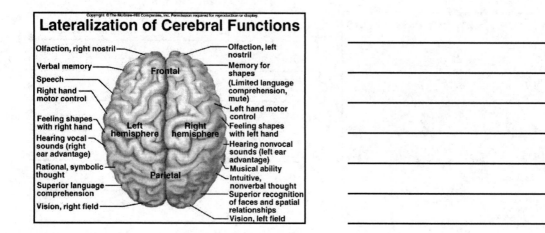

Lateralization of Cerebral Functions

Olfaction, right nostril

Verbal memory

Speech

Right hand motor control

Feeling shapes with right hand

Hearing vocal sounds (right ear advantage)

Rational, symbolic thought

Superior language comprehension

Vision, right field

Frontal

Left hemisphere

Right hemisphere

Parietal

Olfaction, left nostril

Memory for shapes (Limited language comprehension, mute)

Left hand motor control

Feeling shapes with left hand

Hearing nonvocal sounds (left ear advantage)

Musical ability

Intuitive, nonverbal thought

Superior recognition of faces and spatial relationships

Vision, left field

Chapter 15

Anatomy and Physiology: The Unity of Form and Function

Second Edition

Kenneth S. Saladin

(c) The McGraw-Hill Companies, Inc.

Nerve Structure

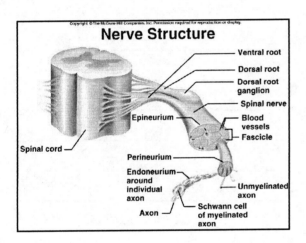

Ganglion Structure

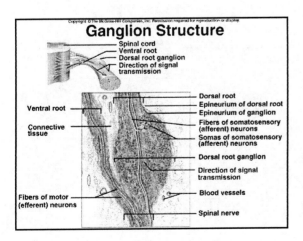

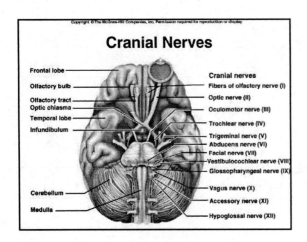

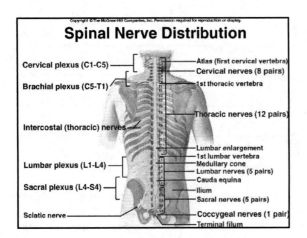

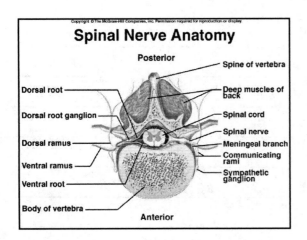

94

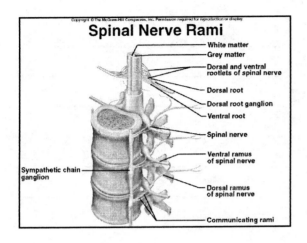

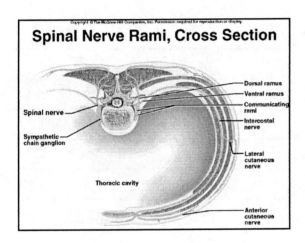

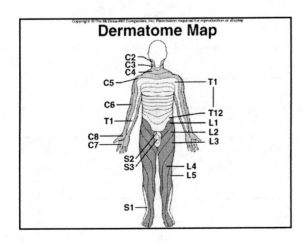

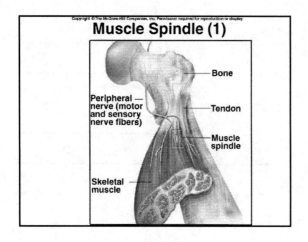

Muscle Spindle (1)

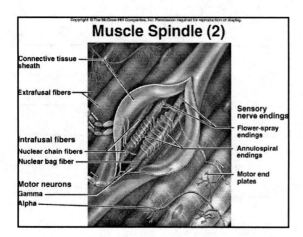

Muscle Spindle (2)

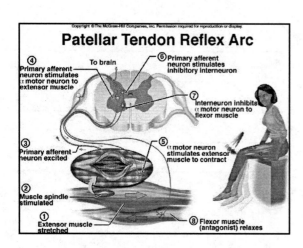

Patellar Tendon Reflex Arc

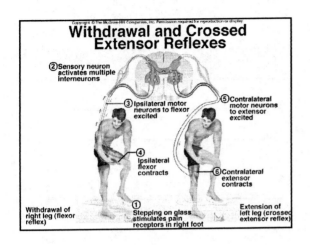

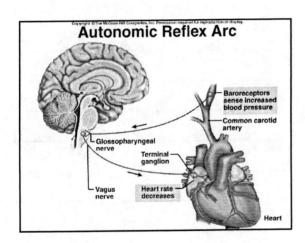

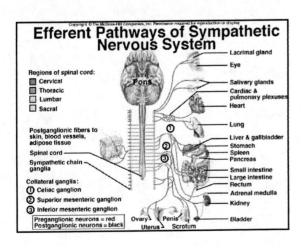

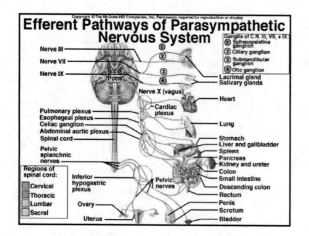

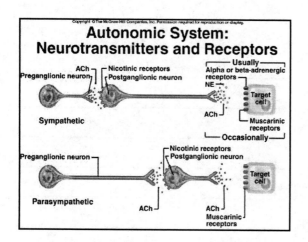

Chapter 16

Anatomy and Physiology: The Unity of Form and Function

Second Edition

Kenneth S. Saladin

(c) The McGraw-Hill Companies, Inc.

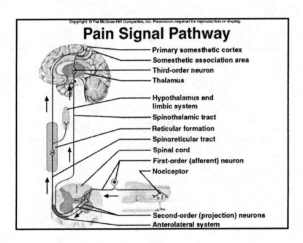

Pain Signal Pathway

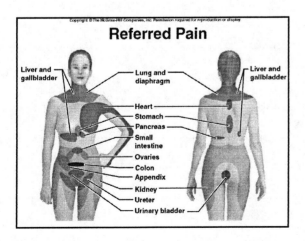

Referred Pain

Taste Receptors

Tongue and papillae

- Epiglottis
- Lingual tonsil
- Palatine tonsil
- Vallate papillae
- Foliate papillae
- Fungiform papillae

Vallate papillae

- Papillae
- Taste buds

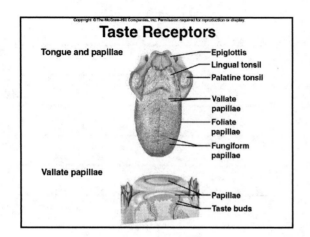

_____

_____

_____

_____

_____

_____

Taste Buds

Lingual papilla

Taste pore

Taste buds

© The McGraw-Hill Companies, Inc./Dennis Strete, photographer

40 µm

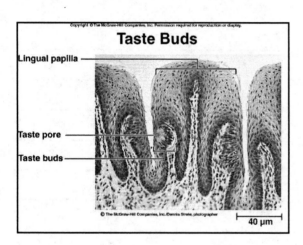

_____

_____

_____

_____

_____

_____

Taste Bud Structure

Connective tissue

Sensory nerve fiber

Taste bud

- Epithelium of tongue
- Basal cell
- Supporting cell
- Gustatory (taste) cell
- Taste hair
- Taste pore

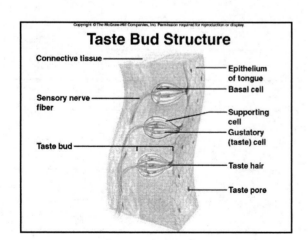

_____

_____

_____

_____

_____

_____

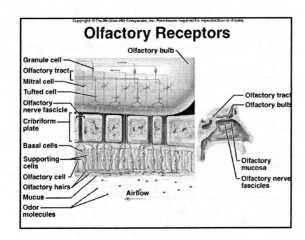

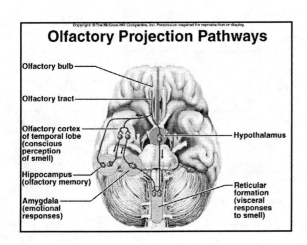

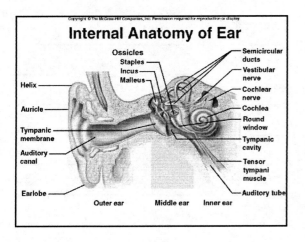

Anatomy of Inner Ear (1)

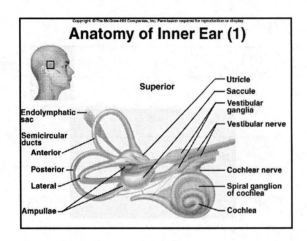

Superior

Utricle
Saccule
Vestibular ganglia
Vestibular nerve

Endolymphatic sac
Semicircular ducts
Anterior
Posterior
Lateral
Ampullae

Cochlear nerve
Spiral ganglion of cochlea
Cochlea

_____

_____

_____

_____

_____

_____

_____

Anatomy of Inner Ear (2)

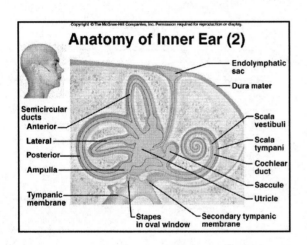

Endolymphatic sac
Dura mater

Semicircular ducts
Anterior
Lateral
Posterior
Ampulla

Tympanic membrane

Stapes in oval window

Secondary tympanic membrane

Scala vestibuli
Scala tympani
Cochlear duct
Saccule
Utricle

_____

_____

_____

_____

_____

_____

Anatomy of the Cochlea

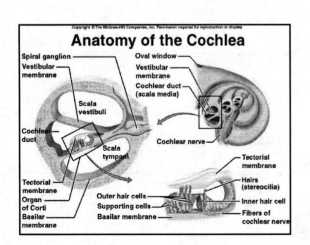

Spiral ganglion
Vestibular membrane

Oval window
Vestibular membrane
Cochlear duct (scala media)

Scala vestibuli

Cochlear duct

Scala tympani

Cochlear nerve

Tectorial membrane
Organ of Corti
Basilar membrane

Outer hair cells
Supporting cells
Basilar membrane

Tectorial membrane
Hairs (stereocilia)
Inner hair cell
Fibers of cochlear nerve

_____

_____

_____

_____

_____

_____

_____

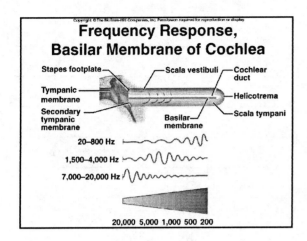

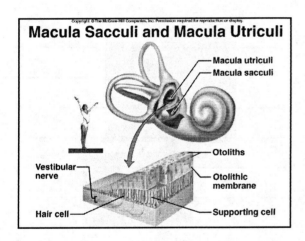

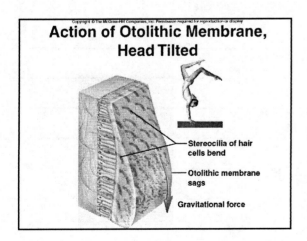

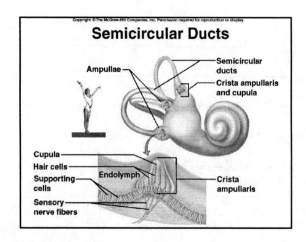

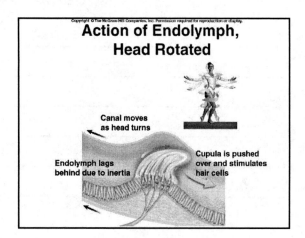

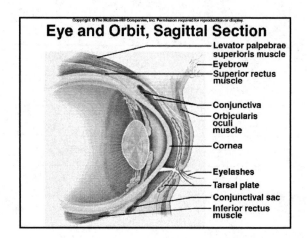

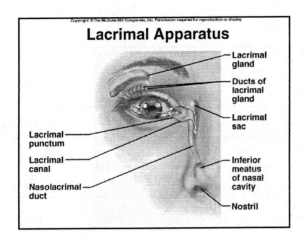

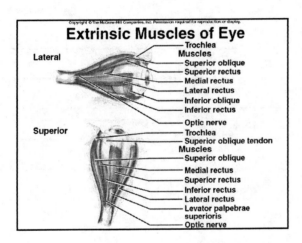

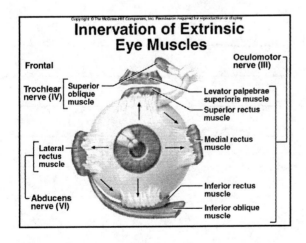

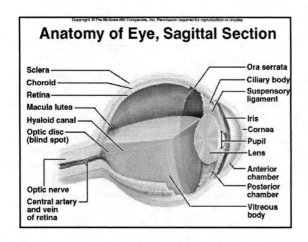

Anatomy of Eye, Sagittal Section

Sclera
Choroid
Retina
Macula lutea
Hyaloid canal
Optic disc (blind spot)
Optic nerve
Central artery and vein of retina
Ora serrata
Ciliary body
Suspensory ligament
Iris
Cornea
Pupil
Lens
Anterior chamber
Posterior chamber
Vitreous body

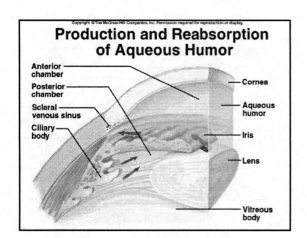

Production and Reabsorption of Aqueous Humor

Anterior chamber
Posterior chamber
Scleral venous sinus
Ciliary body
Cornea
Aqueous humor
Iris
Lens
Vitreous body

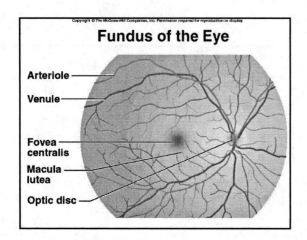

Fundus of the Eye

Arteriole
Venule
Fovea centralis
Macula lutea
Optic disc

Accommodation of Lens

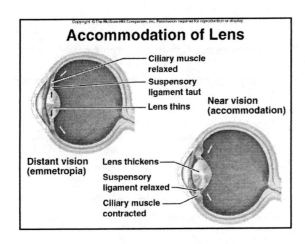

Ciliary muscle relaxed
Suspensory ligament taut
Lens thins
Near vision (accommodation)
Distant vision (emmetropia)
Lens thickens
Suspensory ligament relaxed
Ciliary muscle contracted

Retinal Cells, Schematic

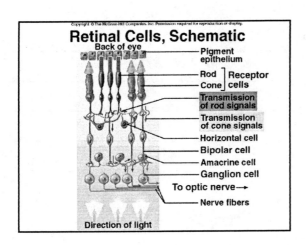

Back of eye
Pigment epithelium
Rod
Cone
Receptor cells
Transmission of rod signals
Transmission of cone signals
Horizontal cell
Bipolar cell
Amacrine cell
Ganglion cell
To optic nerve →
Nerve fibers
Direction of light

Bleaching and Regeneration of Rhodopsin

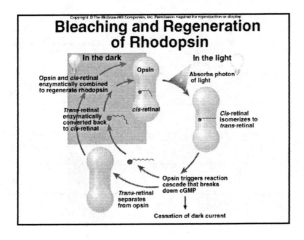

In the dark
In the light
Opsin
Opsin and cis-retinal enzymatically combined to regenerate rhodopsin
Absorbs photon of light
cis-retinal
Trans-retinal enzymatically converted back to cis-retinal
Cis-retinal isomerizes to trans-retinal
Opsin triggers reaction cascade that breaks down cGMP
Trans-retinal separates from opsin
Cessation of dark current

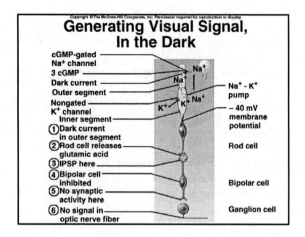

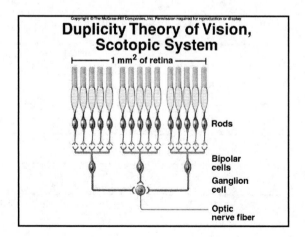

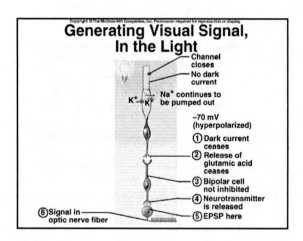

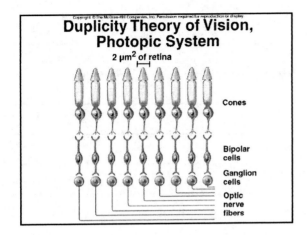

Duplicity Theory of Vision, Photopic System

$2\ \mu m^2$ of retina

Cones

Bipolar cells

Ganglion cells

Optic nerve fibers

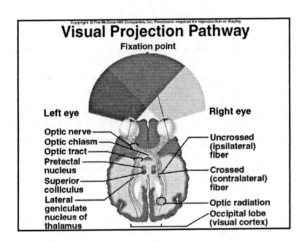

Visual Projection Pathway

Fixation point

Left eye

Right eye

Optic nerve
Optic chiasm
Optic tract
Pretectal nucleus
Superior colliculus
Lateral geniculate nucleus of thalamus

Uncrossed (ipsilateral) fiber
Crossed (contralateral) fiber
Optic radiation
Occipital lobe (visual cortex)

Chapter 17

Anatomy and Physiology: The Unity of Form and Function
Second Edition

Kenneth S. Saladin

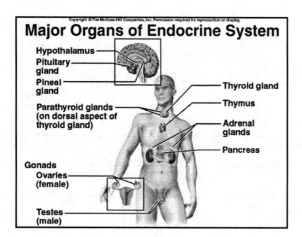

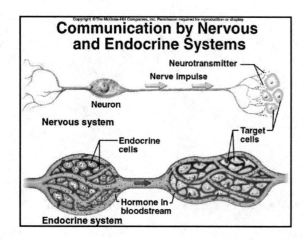

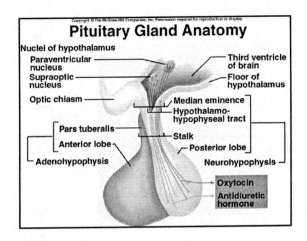

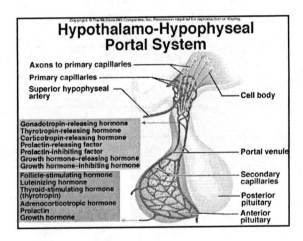

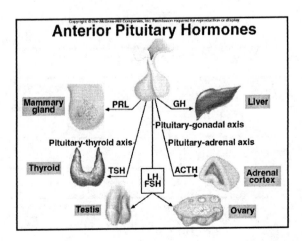

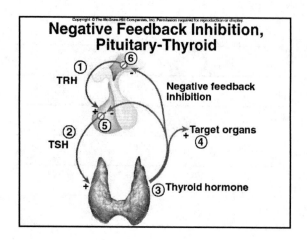

Negative Feedback Inhibition, Pituitary-Thyroid

① TRH
⑥
Negative feedback inhibition
⑤
② TSH
→ Target organs ④
③ Thyroid hormone

Pituitary Dwarfism

© Danile Margulies

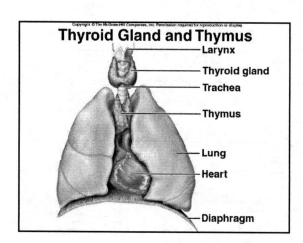

Thyroid Gland and Thymus

Larynx
Thyroid gland
Trachea
Thymus
Lung
Heart
Diaphragm

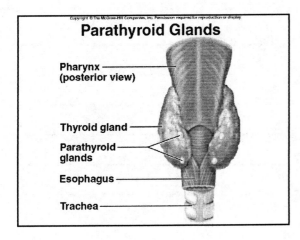

Parathyroid Glands

Pharynx (posterior view)

Thyroid gland

Parathyroid glands

Esophagus

Trachea

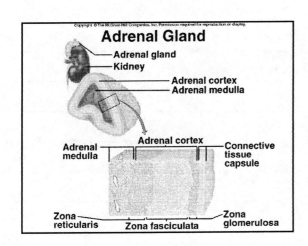

Adrenal Gland

Adrenal gland

Kidney

Adrenal cortex

Adrenal medulla

Adrenal medulla

Adrenal cortex

Connective tissue capsule

Zona reticularis

Zona fasciculata

Zona glomerulosa

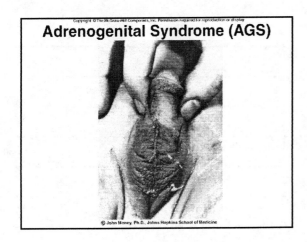

Adrenogenital Syndrome (AGS)

© John Money, Ph.D., Johns Hopkins School of Medicine

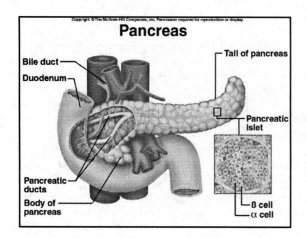

Pancreas

Bile duct
Duodenum
Tail of pancreas
Pancreatic islet
Pancreatic ducts
Body of pancreas
β cell
α cell

_____
_____
_____
_____
_____
_____
_____

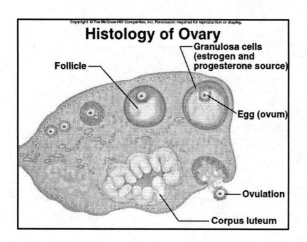

Histology of Ovary

Granulosa cells (estrogen and progesterone source)
Follicle
Egg (ovum)
Ovulation
Corpus luteum

_____
_____
_____
_____
_____
_____
_____

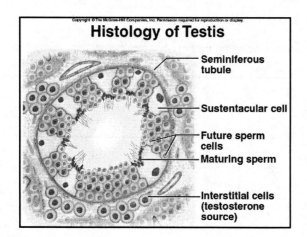

Histology of Testis

Seminiferous tubule
Sustentacular cell
Future sperm cells
Maturing sperm
Interstitial cells (testosterone source)

_____
_____
_____
_____
_____
_____
_____

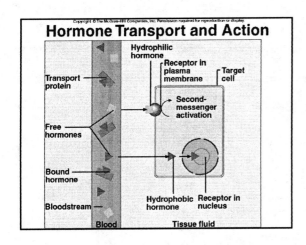

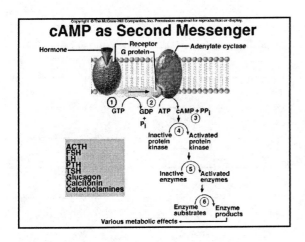

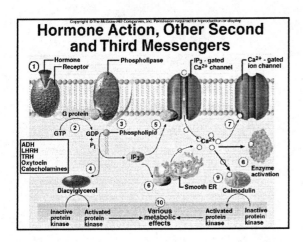

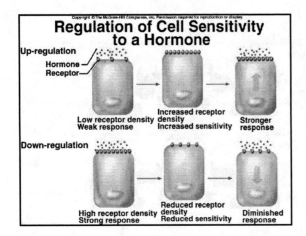

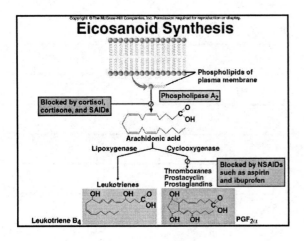

Chapter 18

Anatomy and Physiology: The Unity of Form and Function

Second Edition

Kenneth S. Saladin

Formed Elements of Blood

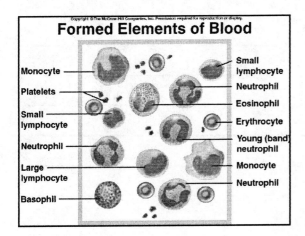

Hemopoiesis

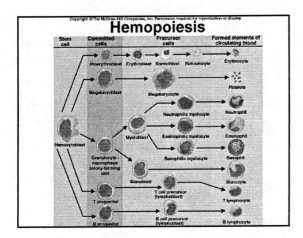

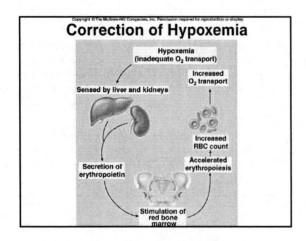

Correction of Hypoxemia

Hypoxemia
(inadequate O_2 transport)

Sensed by liver and kidneys

Increased
O_2 transport

Secretion of
erythropoietin

Increased
RBC count

Accelerated
erythropoiesis

Stimulation of
red bone
marrow

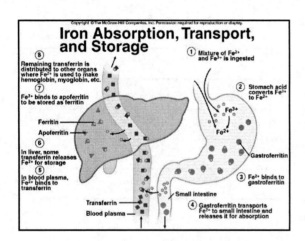

Iron Absorption, Transport, and Storage

⑧ Remaining transferrin is distributed to other organs where Fe^{2+} is used to make hemoglobin, myoglobin, etc.

① Mixture of Fe^{2+} and Fe^{3+} is ingested

② Stomach acid converts Fe^{3+} to Fe^{2+}

⑦ Fe^{3+} binds to apoferritin to be stored as ferritin

Fe^{3+}

Fe^{2+}

Ferritin

Apoferritin

⑥ In liver, some transferrin releases Fe^{2+} for storage

Gastroferritin

⑤ In blood plasma, Fe^{2+} binds to transferrin

Small intestine

③ Fe^{2+} binds to gastroferritin

Transferrin

Blood plasma

④ Gastroferritin transports Fe^{2+} to small intestine and releases it for absorption

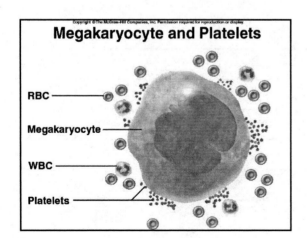

Megakaryocyte and Platelets

RBC

Megakaryocyte

WBC

Platelets

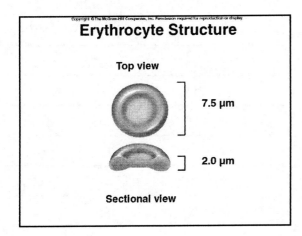

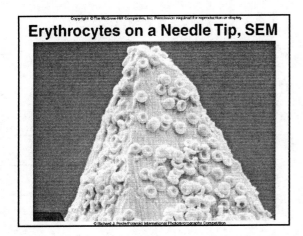

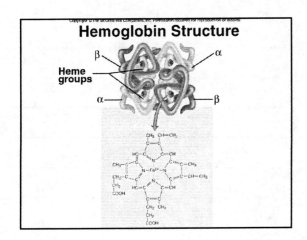

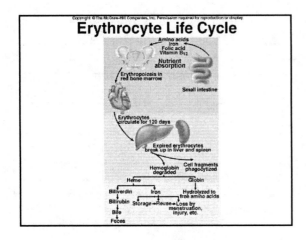

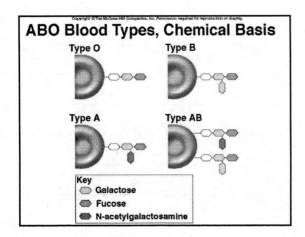

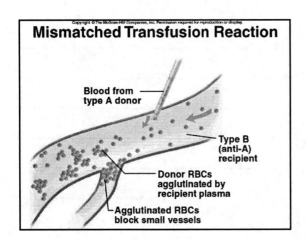

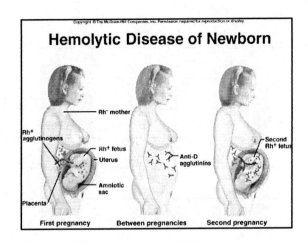

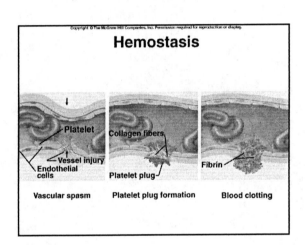

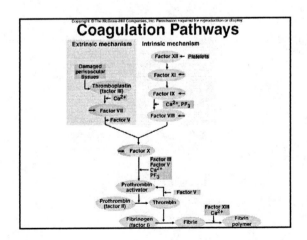

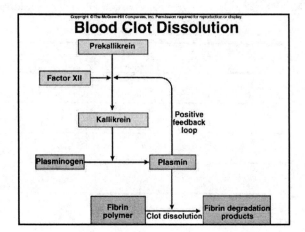

Blood Clot Dissolution

Prekallikrein

Factor XII

Kallikrein

Positive feedback loop

Plasminogen

Plasmin

Fibrin polymer

Clot dissolution

Fibrin degradation products

Chapter 19

Anatomy and Physiology: The Unity of Form and Function
Second Edition

Kenneth S. Saladin

Cardiovascular System, Schematic

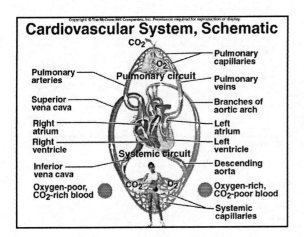

- CO_2
- O_2
- Pulmonary circuit
- Pulmonary arteries
- Superior vena cava
- Right atrium
- Right ventricle
- Systemic circuit
- Inferior vena cava
- Oxygen-poor, CO_2-rich blood
- CO_2
- O_2
- Pulmonary capillaries
- Pulmonary veins
- Branches of aortic arch
- Left atrium
- Left ventricle
- Descending aorta
- Oxygen-rich, CO_2-poor blood
- Systemic capillaries

Heart Position in Thoracic Cavity (1)

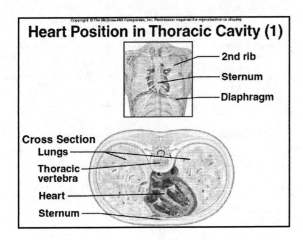

- 2nd rib
- Sternum
- Diaphragm
- Cross Section
- Lungs
- Thoracic vertebra
- Heart
- Sternum

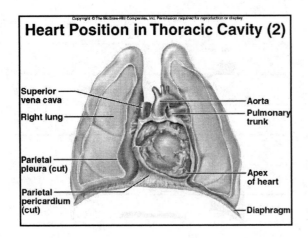

Heart Position in Thoracic Cavity (2)

- Superior vena cava
- Right lung
- Parietal pleura (cut)
- Parietal pericardium (cut)
- Aorta
- Pulmonary trunk
- Apex of heart
- Diaphragm

_____

_____

_____

_____

_____

_____

_____

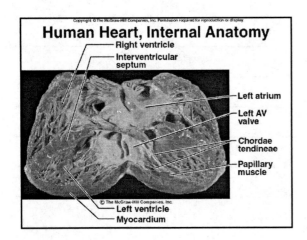

Human Heart, Anterior Aspect

- Fat in interventricular sulcus
- Left ventricle
- Right ventricle
- Anterior interventricular artery

_____

_____

_____

_____

_____

_____

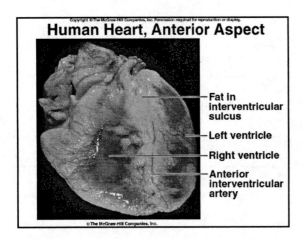

Human Heart, Internal Anatomy

- Right ventricle
- Interventricular septum
- Left atrium
- Left AV valve
- Chordae tendineae
- Papillary muscle
- Left ventricle
- Myocardium

_____

_____

_____

_____

_____

_____

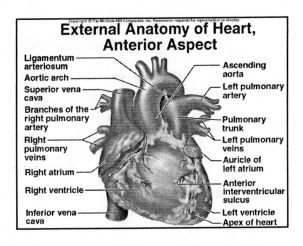

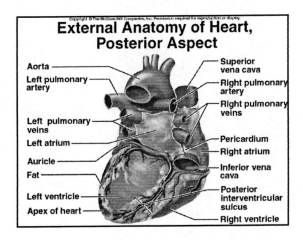

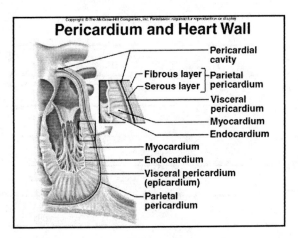

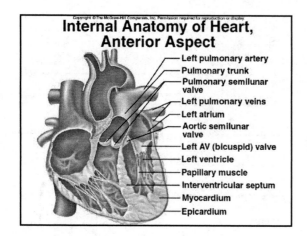

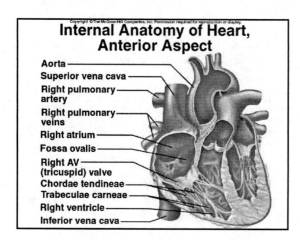

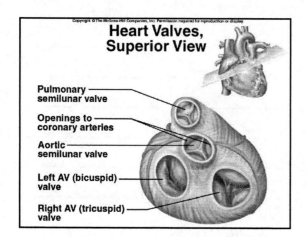

Heart Valves

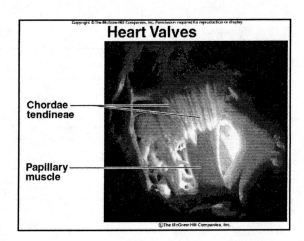

Chordae tendineae

Papillary muscle

Operation of Semilunar Valves

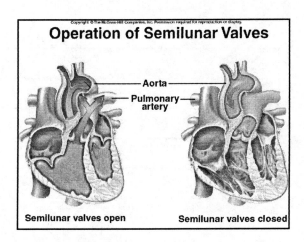

Aorta

Pulmonary artery

Semilunar valves open   Semilunar valves closed

Operation of Atrioventricular Valves

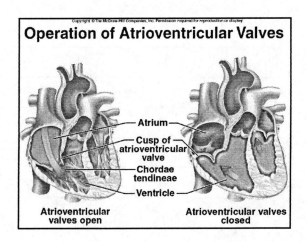

Atrium

Cusp of atrioventricular valve

Chordae tendineae

Ventricle

Atrioventricular valves open   Atrioventricular valves closed

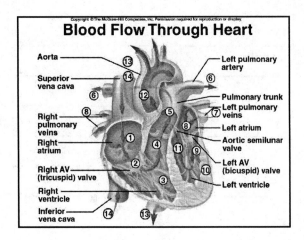

Blood Flow Through Heart

Aorta — ⑬
Superior vena cava — ⑭
⑥
⑫
⑧
⑤
①
④ ⑪
②
③
Right pulmonary veins
Right atrium
Right AV (tricuspid) valve
Right ventricle
Inferior vena cava — ⑭ ⑬

Left pulmonary artery
⑥
Pulmonary trunk
Left pulmonary veins ⑦
⑧ Left atrium
⑨ Aortic semilunar valve
⑩ Left AV (bicuspid) valve
Left ventricle

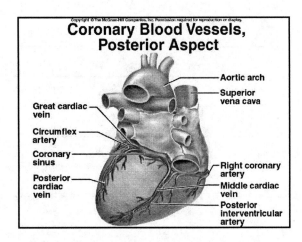

Coronary Blood Vessels, Posterior Aspect

Aortic arch
Superior vena cava
Great cardiac vein
Circumflex artery
Coronary sinus
Posterior cardiac vein
Right coronary artery
Middle cardiac vein
Posterior interventricular artery

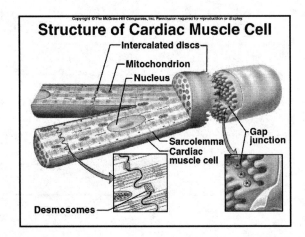

Structure of Cardiac Muscle Cell

Intercalated discs
Mitochondrion
Nucleus
Sarcolemma
Cardiac muscle cell
Gap junction
Desmosomes

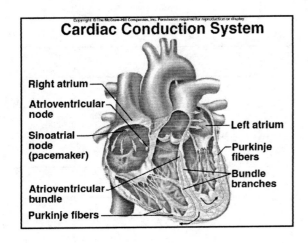

Cardiac Conduction System

Right atrium

Atrioventricular node

Sinoatrial node (pacemaker)

Atrioventricular bundle

Purkinje fibers

Left atrium

Purkinje fibers

Bundle branches

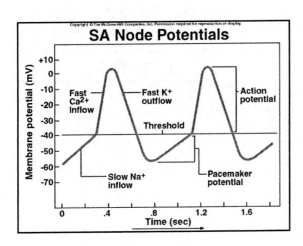

SA Node Potentials

Membrane potential (mV)

Fast Ca²⁺ inflow

Fast K⁺ outflow

Action potential

Threshold

Slow Na⁺ inflow

Pacemaker potential

Time (sec)

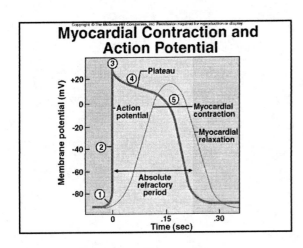

Myocardial Contraction and Action Potential

Membrane potential (mV)

Plateau

Action potential

Myocardial contraction

Myocardial relaxation

Absolute refractory period

Time (sec)

Normal Electrocardiogram (ECG)

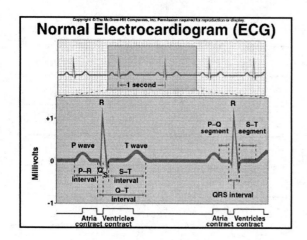

Cardiac Cycle

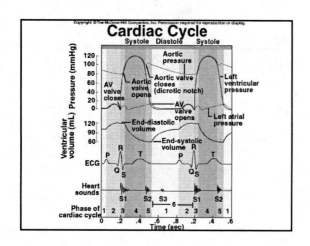

Chapter 20

Anatomy and Physiology: The Unity of Form and Function
Second Edition

Kenneth S. Saladin

Circulatory Pathways

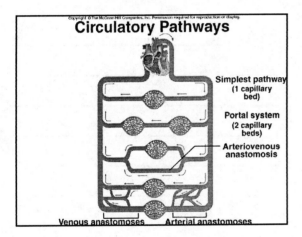

Simplest pathway (1 capillary bed)

Portal system (2 capillary beds)

Arteriovenous anastomosis

Venous anastomoses   Arterial anastomoses

Blood Vessel Structure (1)

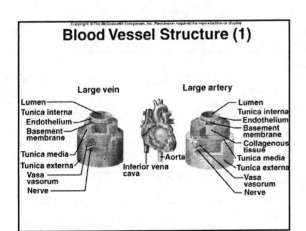

Large vein   Large artery

Lumen
Tunica interna
Endothelium
Basement membrane
Tunica media
Tunica externa
Vasa vasorum
Nerve

Aorta
Inferior vena cava

Lumen
Tunica interna
Endothelium
Basement membrane
Collagenous tissue
Tunica media
Tunica externa
Vasa vasorum
Nerve

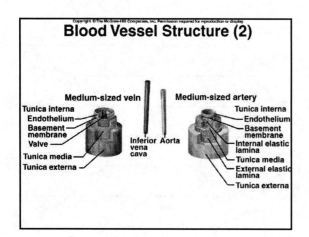

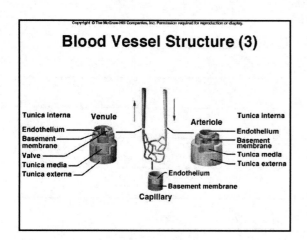

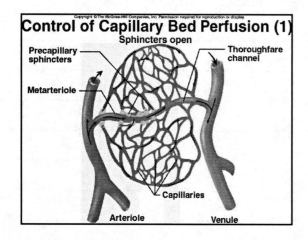

Control of Capillary Bed Perfusion (2)

Sphincters closed

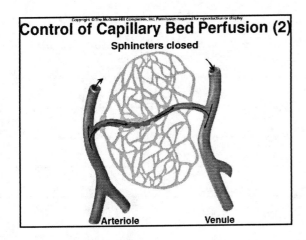

Arteriole   Venule

Distribution of Blood, Resting Adult

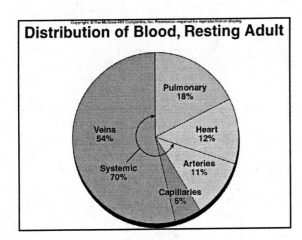

Pulmonary 18%

Veins 54%

Heart 12%

Systemic 70%

Arteries 11%

Capillaries 5%

Relationship of Blood Pressure to Distance from Heart

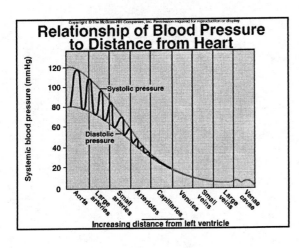

Systemic blood pressure (mmHg)

Systolic pressure

Diastolic pressure

Aorta, Large arteries, Small arteries, Arterioles, Capillaries, Venules, Small veins, Large veins, Venae cavae

Increasing distance from left ventricle

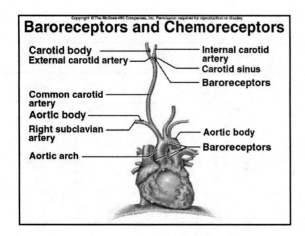

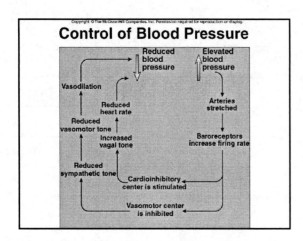

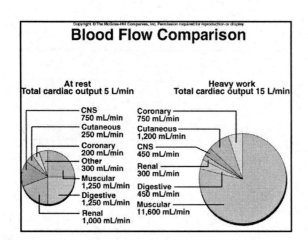

Capillary Filtration and Reabsorption

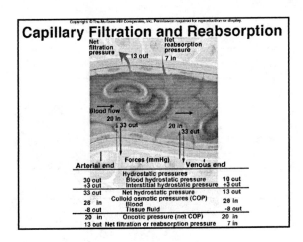

Skeletal Muscle Pump

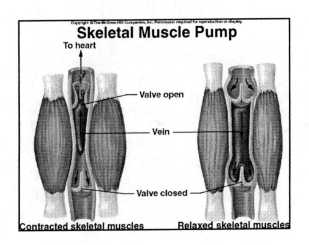

Anatomy of Pulmonary Circulation

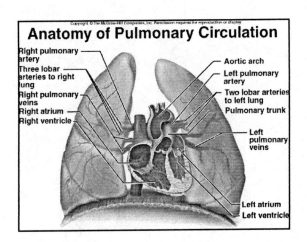

135

Blood Vessels Around Pulmonary Alveoli

Pulmonary vein (to left atrium)
Pulmonary artery (from right ventricle)
Alveolar sacs and alveoli

Chapter 21

Anatomy and Physiology: The Unity of Form and Function
Second Edition

Kenneth S. Saladin

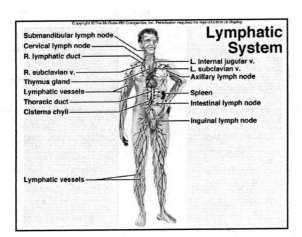

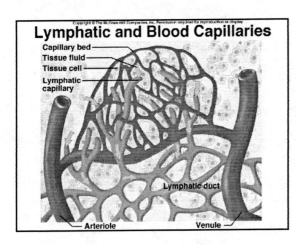

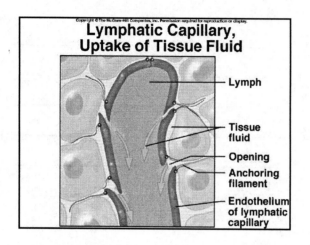

Lymphatic Capillary, Uptake of Tissue Fluid

- Lymph
- Tissue fluid
- Opening
- Anchoring filament
- Endothelium of lymphatic capillary

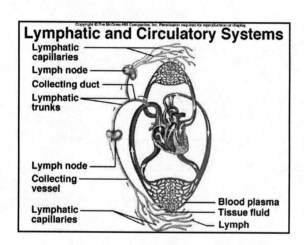

Lymphatic and Circulatory Systems

- Lymphatic capillaries
- Lymph node
- Collecting duct
- Lymphatic trunks
- Lymph node
- Collecting vessel
- Lymphatic capillaries
- Blood plasma
- Tissue fluid
- Lymph

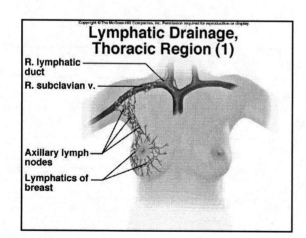

Lymphatic Drainage, Thoracic Region (1)

- R. lymphatic duct
- R. subclavian v.
- Axillary lymph nodes
- Lymphatics of breast

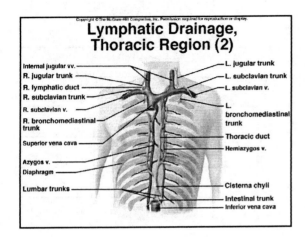

Lymphatic Drainage, Thoracic Region (2)

Internal jugular vv.
R. jugular trunk
R. lymphatic duct
R. subclavian trunk
R. subclavian v.
R. bronchomediastinal trunk
Superior vena cava
Azygos v.
Diaphragm
Lumbar trunks

L. jugular trunk
L. subclavian trunk
L. subclavian v.
L. bronchomediastinal trunk
Thoracic duct
Hemiazygos v.
Cisterna chyli
Intestinal trunk
Inferior vena cava

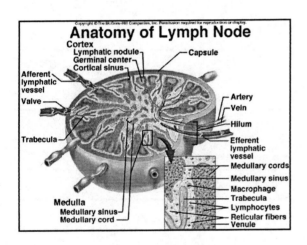

Anatomy of Lymph Node

Cortex
Lymphatic nodule
Germinal center
Cortical sinus
Afferent lymphatic vessel
Valve
Trabecula
Capsule
Artery
Vein
Hilum
Efferent lymphatic vessel
Medullary cords
Medullary sinus
Macrophage
Trabecula
Lymphocytes
Reticular fibers
Venule
Medulla
Medullary sinus
Medullary cord

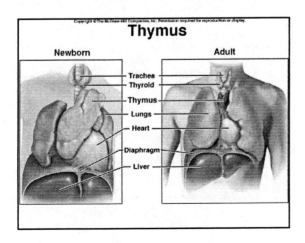

Thymus

Newborn

Adult

Trachea
Thyroid
Thymus
Lungs
Heart
Diaphragm
Liver

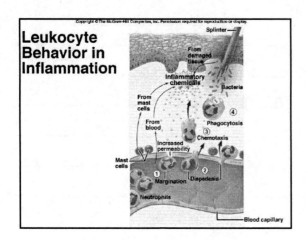

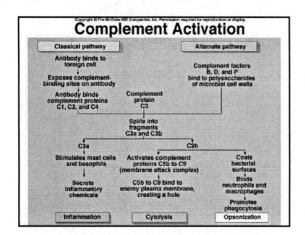

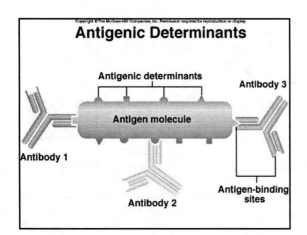

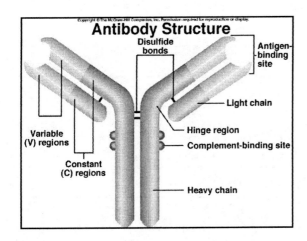

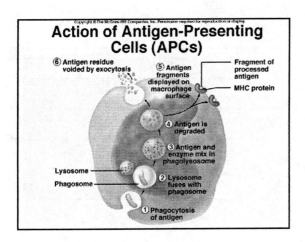

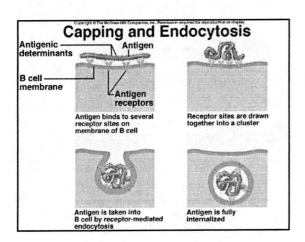

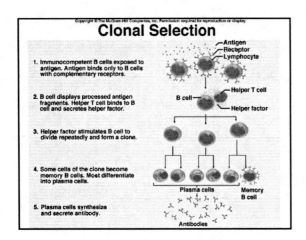

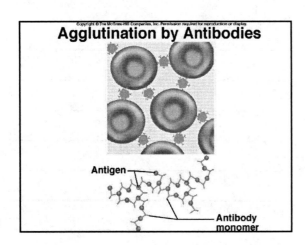

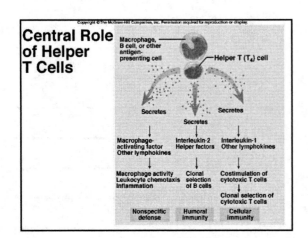

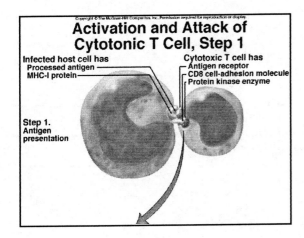

Activation and Attack of Cytotonic T Cell, Step 1

Infected host cell has
Processed antigen
MHC-I protein

Cytotoxic T cell has
Antigen receptor
CD8 cell-adhesion molecule
Protein kinase enzyme

Step 1.
Antigen
presentation

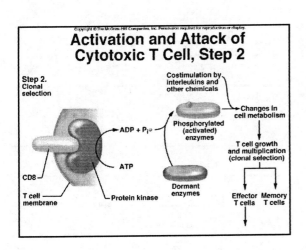

Activation and Attack of Cytotoxic T Cell, Step 2

Step 2.
Clonal
selection

CD8

T cell
membrane

Protein kinase

Dormant
enzymes

ADP + P$_i$

ATP

Phosphorylated
(activated)
enzymes

Costimulation by
interleukins and
other chemicals

Changes in
cell metabolism

T cell growth
and multiplication
(clonal selection)

Effector
T cells

Memory
T cells

Chapter 22

Anatomy and Physiology: The Unity of Form and Function
Second Edition

Kenneth S. Saladin

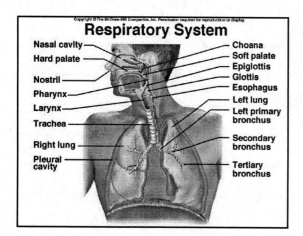

Respiratory System

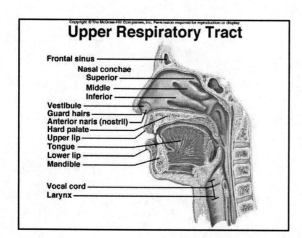

Upper Respiratory Tract

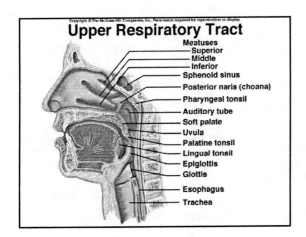

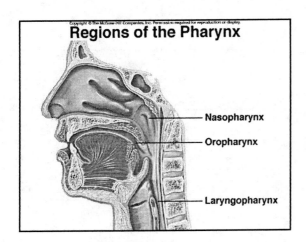

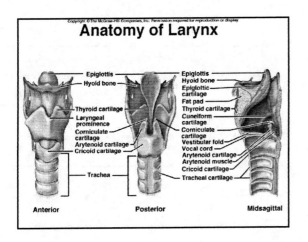

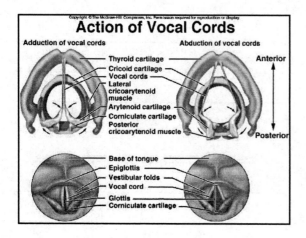

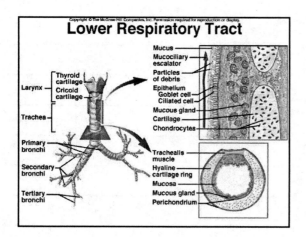

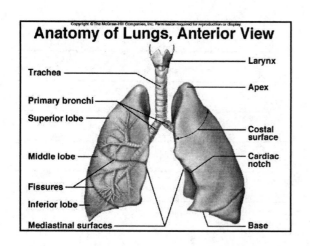

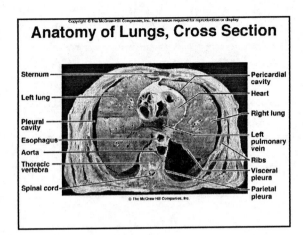

Anatomy of Lungs, Cross Section

Sternum
Left lung
Pleural cavity
Esophagus
Aorta
Thoracic vertebra
Spinal cord

Pericardial cavity
Heart
Right lung
Left pulmonary vein
Ribs
Visceral pleura
Parietal pleura

_____

_____

_____

_____

_____

_____

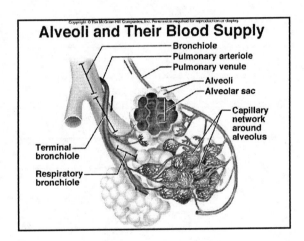

Alveoli and Their Blood Supply

Bronchiole
Pulmonary arteriole
Pulmonary venule
Alveoli
Alveolar sac
Capillary network around alveolus
Terminal bronchiole
Respiratory bronchiole

_____

_____

_____

_____

_____

_____

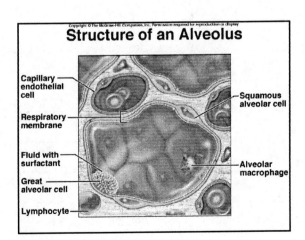

Structure of an Alveolus

Capillary endothelial cell
Respiratory membrane
Fluid with surfactant
Great alveolar cell
Lymphocyte

Squamous alveolar cell
Alveolar macrophage

_____

_____

_____

_____

_____

_____

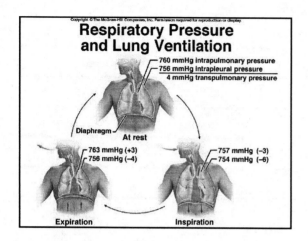

Respiratory Pressure and Lung Ventilation

760 mmHg intrapulmonary pressure
756 mmHg intrapleural pressure
4 mmHg transpulmonary pressure

Diaphragm
At rest

763 mmHg (+3)
756 mmHg (−4)

757 mmHg (−3)
754 mmHg (−6)

Expiration

Inspiration

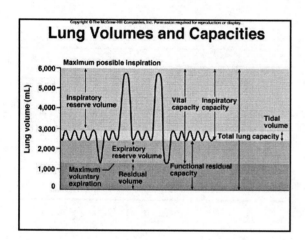

Lung Volumes and Capacities

Lung volume (mL)

Maximum possible inspiration

Inspiratory reserve volume

Vital capacity

Inspiratory capacity

Tidal volume

Total lung capacity

Expiratory reserve volume

Maximum voluntary expiration

Residual volume

Functional residual capacity

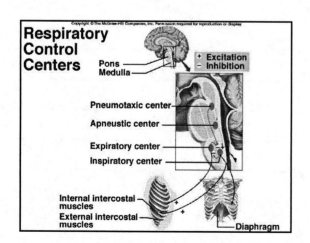

Respiratory Control Centers

Pons
Medulla

+ Excitation
− Inhibition

Pneumotaxic center

Apneustic center

Expiratory center

Inspiratory center

Internal intercostal muscles

External intercostal muscles

Diaphragm

Partial Pressure Changes and Circulation

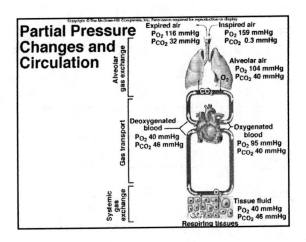

Alveolar gas exchange

Expired air
P_{O_2} 116 mmHg
P_{CO_2} 32 mmHg

Inspired air
P_{O_2} 159 mmHg
P_{CO_2} 0.3 mmHg

Alveolar air
P_{O_2} 104 mmHg
P_{CO_2} 40 mmHg

Gas transport

Deoxygenated blood
P_{O_2} 40 mmHg
P_{CO_2} 46 mmHg

Oxygenated blood
P_{O_2} 95 mmHg
P_{CO_2} 40 mmHg

Systemic gas exchange

Tissue fluid
P_{O_2} 40 mmHg
P_{CO_2} 46 mmHg

Respiring tissues

Oxygen Loading and Concentration Gradient

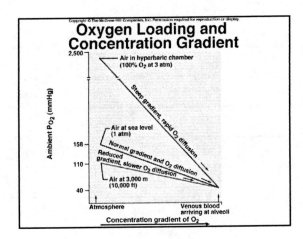

Ambient P_{O_2} (mmHg)

2,500 — Air in hyperbaric chamber (100% O_2 at 3 atm)

Steep gradient, rapid O_2 diffusion

Air at sea level (1 atm)

158 — Normal gradient and O_2 diffusion

110 — Reduced gradient, slower O_2 diffusion

Air at 3,000 m (10,000 ft)

40 —

Atmosphere   Venous blood arriving at alveoli

Concentration gradient of O_2

Ventilation-Perfusion Ratio (1)

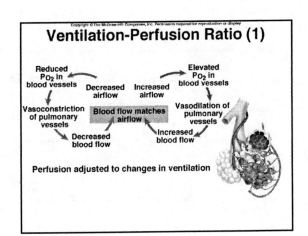

Reduced P_{O_2} in blood vessels

Decreased airflow

Increased airflow

Elevated P_{O_2} in blood vessels

Vasoconstriction of pulmonary vessels

Blood flow matches airflow

Vasodilation of pulmonary vessels

Decreased blood flow

Increased blood flow

Perfusion adjusted to changes in ventilation

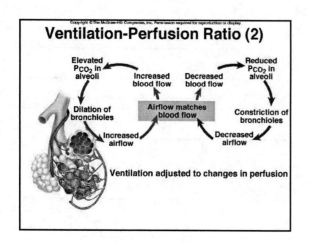

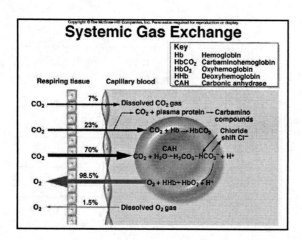

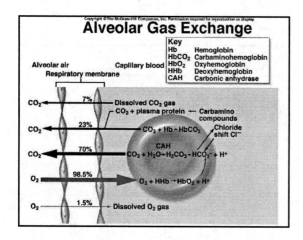

Oxyhemoglobin Dissociation and Temperature

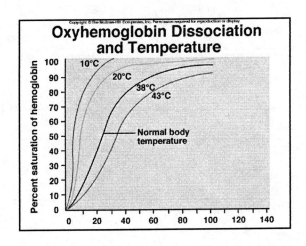

Percent saturation of hemoglobin

10°C
20°C
38°C
43°C

Normal body temperature

Oxyhemoglobin Dissociation and pH

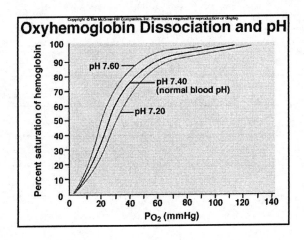

Percent saturation of hemoglobin

pH 7.60
pH 7.40 (normal blood pH)
pH 7.20

P_{O_2} (mmHg)

Peripheral Chemoreceptor Pathways

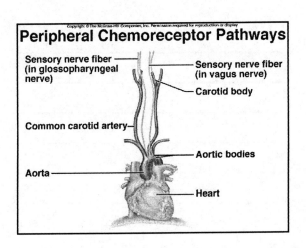

Sensory nerve fiber (in glossopharyngeal nerve)

Sensory nerve fiber (in vagus nerve)

Carotid body

Common carotid artery

Aortic bodies

Aorta

Heart

Chapter 23

Anatomy and Physiology: The Unity of Form and Function
Second Edition

Kenneth S. Saladin

Urinary System

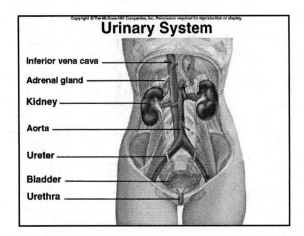

Inferior vena cava
Adrenal gland
Kidney
Aorta
Ureter
Bladder
Urethra

Major Nitrogenous Wastes

Ammonia

Urea

Uric acid

Creatinine

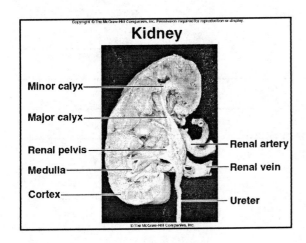

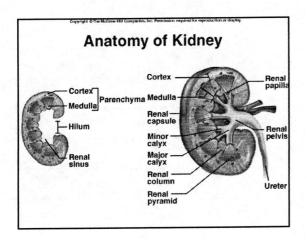

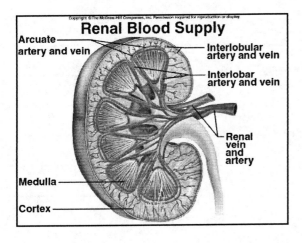

Kidney Lobe

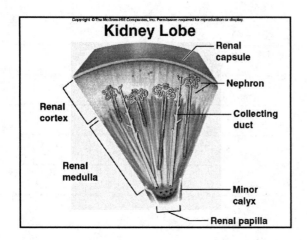

Renal capsule

Nephron

Renal cortex

Collecting duct

Renal medulla

Minor calyx

Renal papilla

_____

_____

_____

_____

_____

_____

Nephron Structure

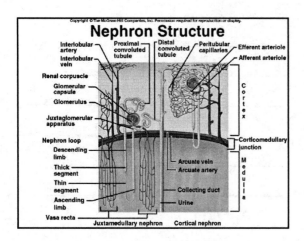

Interlobular artery
Interlobular vein
Renal corpuscle
Glomerular capsule
Glomerulus
Juxtaglomerular apparatus
Nephron loop
Descending limb
Thick segment
Thin segment
Ascending limb
Vasa recta

Proximal convoluted tubule
Distal convoluted tubule
Peritubular capillaries
Efferent arteriole
Afferent arteriole

Cortex
Corticomedullary junction
Medulla

Arcuate vein
Arcuate artery
Collecting duct
Urine

Juxtamedullary nephron   Cortical nephron

_____

_____

_____

_____

_____

_____

Proportions of Nephron Loops

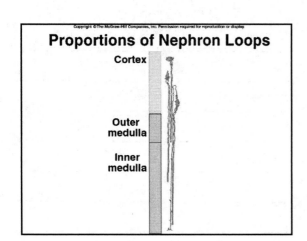

Cortex

Outer medulla

Inner medulla

_____

_____

_____

_____

_____

_____

_____

154

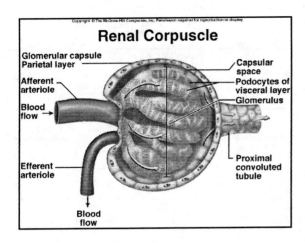

Renal Corpuscle

- Glomerular capsule Parietal layer
- Afferent arteriole
- Blood flow →
- Efferent arteriole
- Blood flow ↓
- Capsular space
- Podocytes of visceral layer
- Glomerulus
- Proximal convoluted tubule

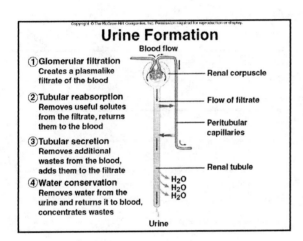

Urine Formation

Blood flow

① Glomerular filtration
Creates a plasmalike filtrate of the blood

② Tubular reabsorption
Removes useful solutes from the filtrate, returns them to the blood

③ Tubular secretion
Removes additional wastes from the blood, adds them to the filtrate

④ Water conservation
Removes water from the urine and returns it to blood, concentrates wastes

- Renal corpuscle
- Flow of filtrate
- Peritubular capillaries
- Renal tubule

H_2O
H_2O
H_2O

Urine

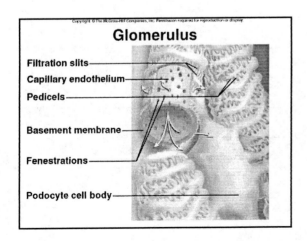

Glomerulus

- Filtration slits
- Capillary endothelium
- Pedicels
- Basement membrane
- Fenestrations
- Podocyte cell body

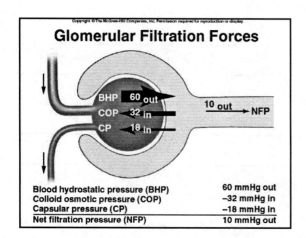

Glomerular Filtration Forces

Blood hydrostatic pressure (BHP)	60 mmHg out
Colloid osmotic pressure (COP)	−32 mmHg in
Capsular pressure (CP)	−18 mmHg in
Net filtration pressure (NFP)	10 mmHg out

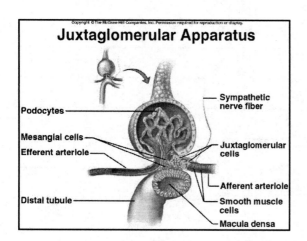

Juxtaglomerular Apparatus

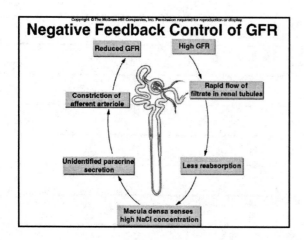

Negative Feedback Control of GFR

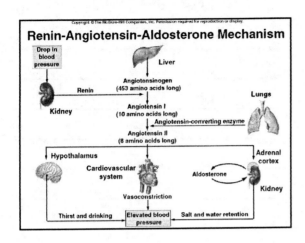

Renin-Angiotensin-Aldosterone Mechanism

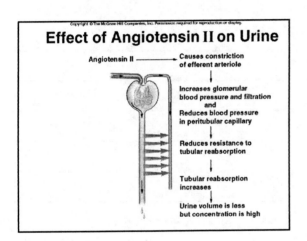

Effect of Angiotensin II on Urine

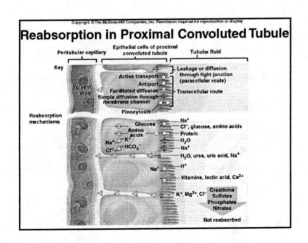

Reabsorption in Proximal Convoluted Tubule

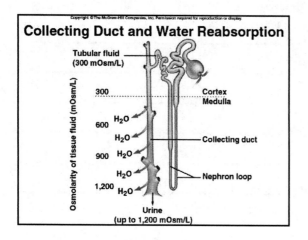

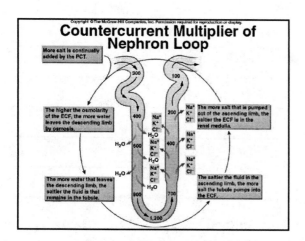

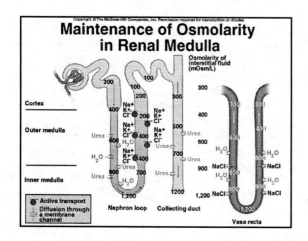

Tubular Reabsorption and Secretion

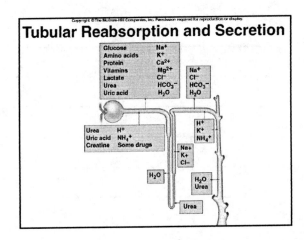

Urinary Bladder and Urethra, Male

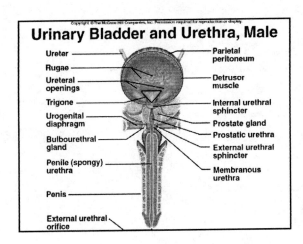

Urinary Bladder and Urethra, Female

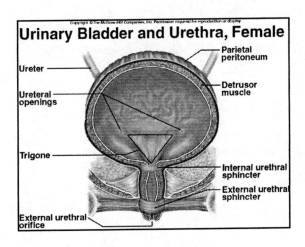

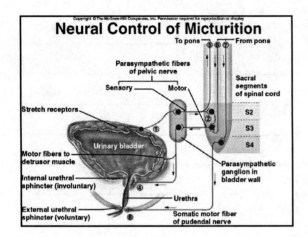

Neural Control of Micturition

Chapter 24

Anatomy and Physiology: The Unity of Form and Function

Second Edition

Kenneth S. Saladin

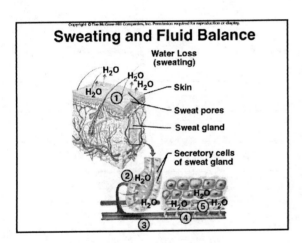

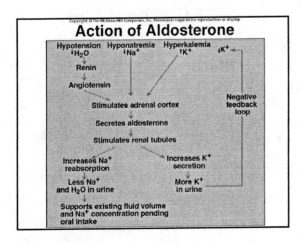

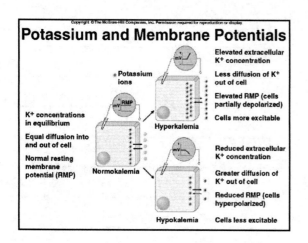

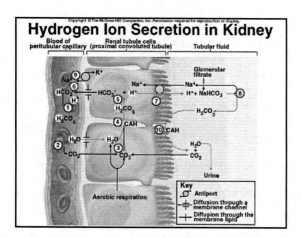

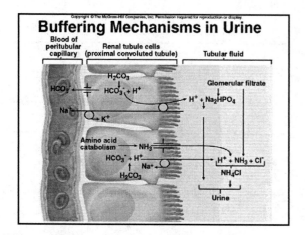

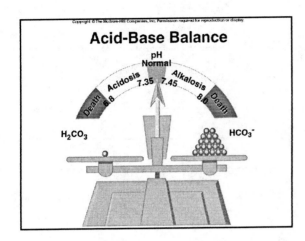

Acid-Base Balance

pH
Normal

Acidosis   7.35   7.45   Alkalosis

Death   6.8   8.0   Death

H_2CO_3 HCO_3^-

_____

_____

_____

_____

_____

_____

_____

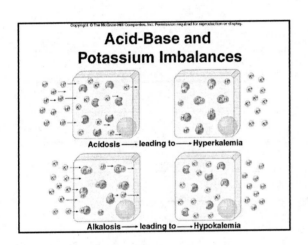

Acid-Base and
Potassium Imbalances

Acidosis —— leading to —— Hyperkalemia

Alkalosis —— leading to —— Hypokalemia

_____

_____

_____

_____

_____

_____

_____

Chapter 25

Anatomy and Physiology: The Unity of Form and Function

Second Edition

Kenneth S. Saladin

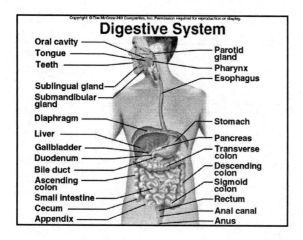

Digestive System

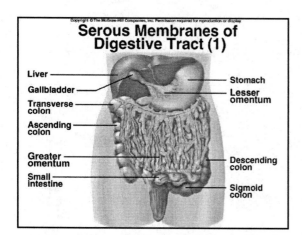

Serous Membranes of Digestive Tract (1)

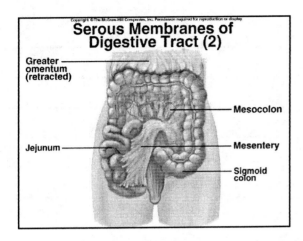

Serous Membranes of Digestive Tract (2)

Greater omentum (retracted)

Jejunum

Mesocolon

Mesentery

Sigmoid colon

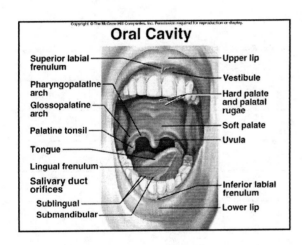

Oral Cavity

Superior labial frenulum

Pharyngopalatine arch

Glossopalatine arch

Palatine tonsil

Tongue

Lingual frenulum

Salivary duct orifices

Sublingual

Submandibular

Upper lip

Vestibule

Hard palate and palatal rugae

Soft palate

Uvula

Inferior labial frenulum

Lower lip

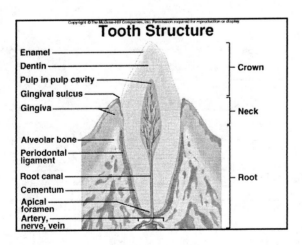

Tooth Structure

Enamel

Dentin

Pulp in pulp cavity

Gingival sulcus

Gingiva

Alveolar bone

Periodontal ligament

Root canal

Cementum

Apical foramen

Artery, nerve, vein

Crown

Neck

Root

Extrinsic Salivary Glands

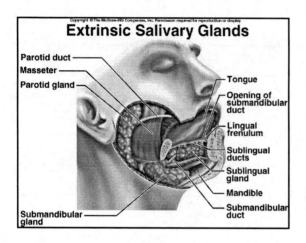

Parotid duct
Masseter
Parotid gland

Tongue
Opening of submandibular duct
Lingual frenulum
Sublingual ducts
Sublingual gland
Mandible
Submandibular duct

Submandibular gland

Anatomy of Esophagus

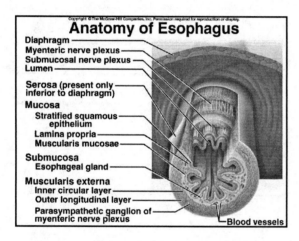

Diaphragm
Myenteric nerve plexus
Submucosal nerve plexus
Lumen
Serosa (present only inferior to diaphragm)
Mucosa
Stratified squamous epithelium
Lamina propria
Muscularis mucosae
Submucosa
Esophageal gland
Muscularis externa
Inner circular layer
Outer longitudinal layer
Parasympathetic ganglion of myenteric nerve plexus
Blood vessels

Swallowing

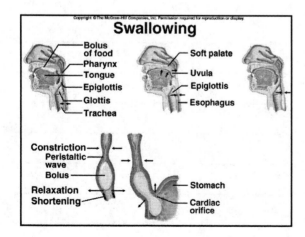

Bolus of food
Pharynx
Tongue
Epiglottis
Glottis
Trachea

Soft palate
Uvula
Epiglottis
Esophagus

Constriction
Peristaltic wave
Bolus
Relaxation
Shortening
Stomach
Cardiac orifice

Swallowing, X ray of Esophagus

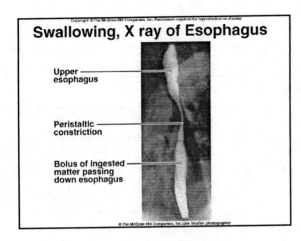

Upper esophagus

Peristaltic constriction

Bolus of ingested matter passing down esophagus

Anatomy of Stomach

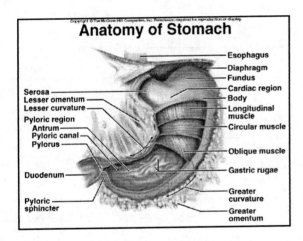

Serosa
Lesser omentum
Lesser curvature
Pyloric region
Antrum
Pyloric canal
Pylorus
Duodenum
Pyloric sphincter

Esophagus
Diaphragm
Fundus
Cardiac region
Body
Longitudinal muscle
Circular muscle
Oblique muscle
Gastric rugae
Greater curvature
Greater omentum

Stomach Wall

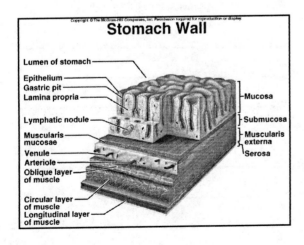

Lumen of stomach
Epithelium
Gastric pit
Lamina propria
Lymphatic nodule
Muscularis mucosae
Venule
Arteriole
Oblique layer of muscle
Circular layer of muscle
Longitudinal layer of muscle

Mucosa
Submucosa
Muscularis externa
Serosa

Gastric Pit and Gastric Gland

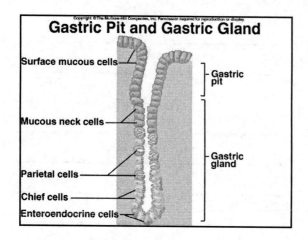

Surface mucous cells — Gastric pit

Mucous neck cells — Gastric gland

Parietal cells —

Chief cells —

Enteroendocrine cells —

_____

_____

_____

_____

_____

_____

Stomach Acid Secretion

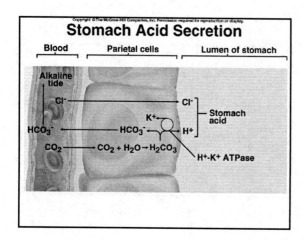

Blood | Parietal cells | Lumen of stomach

Alkaline tide

Cl^- → Cl^- — Stomach acid

HCO_3^- ← HCO_3^- K^+ → H^+

CO_2 → $CO_2 + H_2O$ → H_2CO_3 — H^+-K^+ ATPase

_____

_____

_____

_____

_____

Production and Action of Pepsin

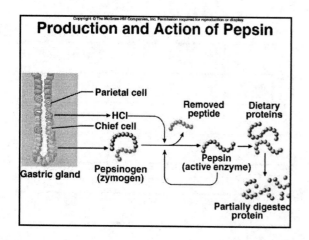

Parietal cell

HCl — Removed peptide — Dietary proteins

Chief cell

Gastric gland — Pepsinogen (zymogen) — Pepsin (active enzyme)

Partially digested protein

_____

_____

_____

_____

_____

_____

_____

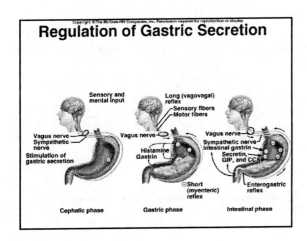

Regulation of Gastric Secretion

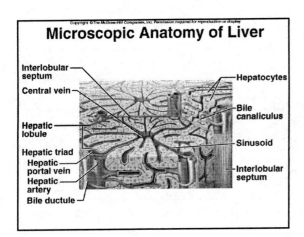

Positive Feedback Control of Gastric Secretion

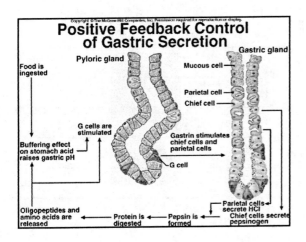

Microscopic Anatomy of Liver

Liver Histology

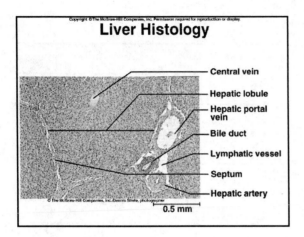

- Central vein
- Hepatic lobule
- Hepatic portal vein
- Bile duct
- Lymphatic vessel
- Septum
- Hepatic artery

© The McGraw-Hill Companies, Inc./Dennis Strete, photographer

0.5 mm

Liver, Gallbladder, and Pancreas

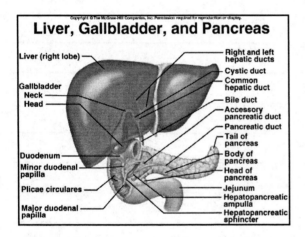

Liver (right lobe)

Gallbladder
Neck
Head

Duodenum
Minor duodenal papilla
Plicae circulares
Major duodenal papilla

Right and left hepatic ducts
Cystic duct
Common hepatic duct
Bile duct
Accessory pancreatic duct
Pancreatic duct
Tail of pancreas
Body of pancreas
Head of pancreas
Jejunum
Hepatopancreatic ampulla
Hepatopancreatic sphincter

Activation of Pancreatic Enzymes

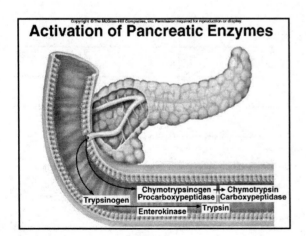

Trypsinogen

Chymotrypsinogen → Chymotrypsin
Procarboxypeptidase → Carboxypeptidase

Enterokinase → Trypsin

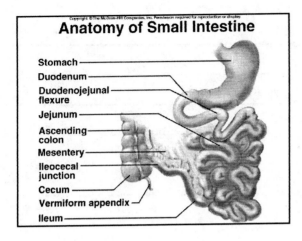

Anatomy of Small Intestine

Stomach
Duodenum
Duodenojejunal flexure
Jejunum
Ascending colon
Mesentery
Ileocecal junction
Cecum
Vermiform appendix
Ileum

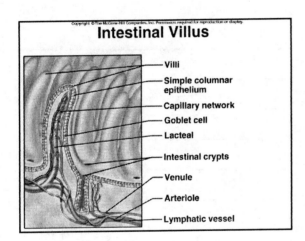

Intestinal Villus

Villi
Simple columnar epithelium
Capillary network
Goblet cell
Lacteal
Intestinal crypts
Venule
Arteriole
Lymphatic vessel

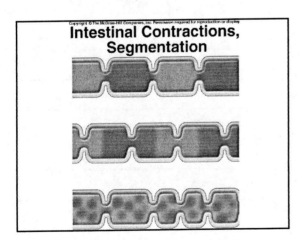

Intestinal Contractions, Segmentation

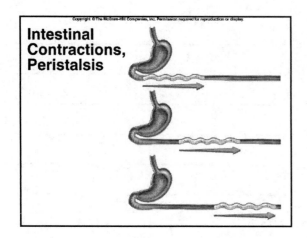

Intestinal Contractions, Peristalsis

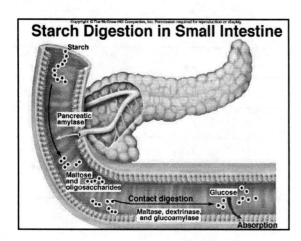

Starch Digestion in Small Intestine

Starch

Pancreatic amylase

Maltose and oligosaccharides

Contact digestion

Maltase, dextrinase, and glucoamylase

Glucose

Absorption

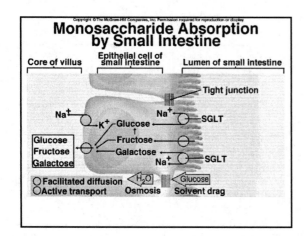

Monosaccharide Absorption by Small Intestine

Core of villus | Epithelial cell of small intestine | Lumen of small intestine

Tight junction

Na⁺   Na⁺   SGLT
K⁺—Glucose
Glucose   Fructose
Fructose   Galactose
Galactose   Na⁺   SGLT

○ Facilitated diffusion   H₂O   Glucose
○ Active transport   Osmosis   Solvent drag

Protein Digestion and Absorption (1)

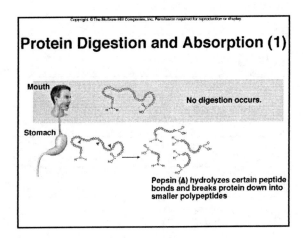

Mouth

No digestion occurs.

Stomach

Pepsin (▲) hydrolyzes certain peptide bonds and breaks protein down into smaller polypeptides

Protein Digestion and Absorption (2)

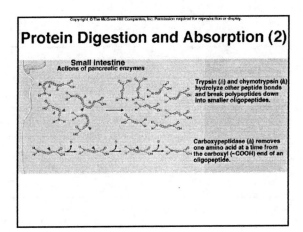

Small intestine
Actions of pancreatic enzymes

Trypsin (▲) and chymotrypsin (▲) hydrolyze other peptide bonds and break polypeptides down into smaller oligopeptides.

Carboxypeptidase (▲) removes one amino acid at a time from the carboxyl (–COOH) end of an oligopeptide.

Protein Digestion and Absorption (3)

Small intestine
Actions of brush border enzymes (contact digestion)

Carboxypeptidase Aminopeptidase Dipeptidase

Blood capillary of intestinal villus

Carboxypeptidase (▲) of the brush border continues to remove amino acids from the carboxyl (–COOH) end.

Aminopeptidase (▲) of the brush border removes one amino acid at a time from the amino (–NH$_2$) end.

Dipeptidase (▲) splits dipeptides (○○) into separate amino acids (○).

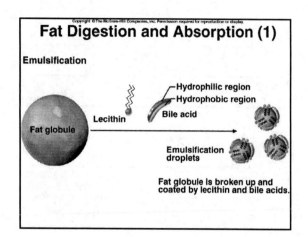

Fat Digestion and Absorption (1)

Emulsification

- Hydrophilic region
- Hydrophobic region
- Bile acid

Fat globule

Lecithin

Emulsification droplets

Fat globule is broken up and coated by lecithin and bile acids.

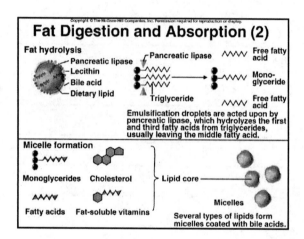

Fat Digestion and Absorption (2)

Fat hydrolysis
- Pancreatic lipase
- Lecithin
- Bile acid
- Dietary lipid

Pancreatic lipase

Free fatty acid

Monoglyceride

Triglyceride

Free fatty acid

Emulsification droplets are acted upon by pancreatic lipase, which hydrolyzes the first and third fatty acids from triglycerides, usually leaving the middle fatty acid.

Micelle formation

Monoglycerides   Cholesterol

Lipid core

Fatty acids   Fat-soluble vitamins

Micelles

Several types of lipids form micelles coated with bile acids.

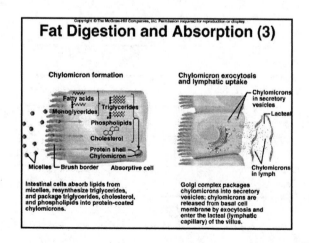

Fat Digestion and Absorption (3)

Chylomicron formation

Fatty acids
Monoglycerides
Triglycerides
Phospholipids
Cholesterol
Protein shell
Chylomicron

Micelles — Brush border   Absorptive cell

Intestinal cells absorb lipids from micelles, resynthesize triglycerides, and package triglycerides, cholesterol, and phospholipids into protein-coated chylomicrons.

Chylomicron exocytosis and lymphatic uptake

- Chylomicrons in secretory vesicles
- Lacteal
- Chylomicrons in lymph

Golgi complex packages chylomicrons into secretory vesicles; chylomicrons are released from basal cell membrane by exocytosis and enter the lacteal (lymphatic capillary) of the villus.

174

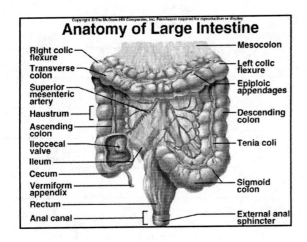

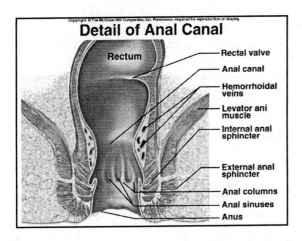

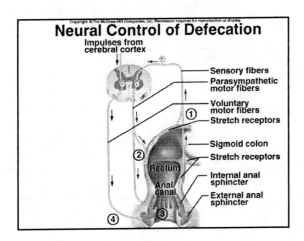

Chapter 26

Anatomy and Physiology: The Unity of Form and Function
Second Edition

Kenneth S. Saladin

Lipoprotein Processing

Chylomicron pathway
Lymph drains into bloodstream
Lymph absorbs chylomicrons from small intestine

VLDL/LDL pathway
Leaves LDLs containing mainly cholesterol

Cells requiring cholesterol absorb LDLs by receptor-mediated endocytosis

Triglycerides are removed and stored in adipocytes

Lipoprotein lipase removes lipids from chylomicrons

Liver produces VLDLs

Liver produces empty HDL shells

Liver disposes of chylomicron remnants

Lipids are stored in adipocytes or used by other cells

HDL shells pick up cholesterol and phospholipids from tissues

Filled HDLs return to liver

Liver excretes cholesterol as bile salts

HDL pathway

Glycolysis Overview

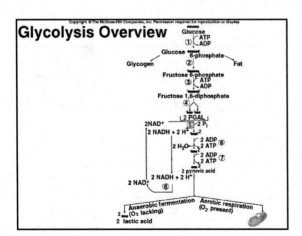

Glucose
① ATP / ADP
Glucose 6-phosphate ②
Glycogen — Fat
Fructose 6-phosphate
③ ATP / ADP
Fructose 1,6-diphosphate
④
2 PGAL
2NAD⁺ ⑤ 2 Pᵢ
2 NADH + 2 H⁺
2 H₂O — 2 ADP / 2 ATP ⑥
2 ADP / 2 ATP ⑦
2 pyruvic acid
2 NADH + 2 H⁺
2 NAD⁺ ⑧
Anaerobic fermentation (O₂ lacking)
Aerobic respiration (O₂ present)
2 lactic acid

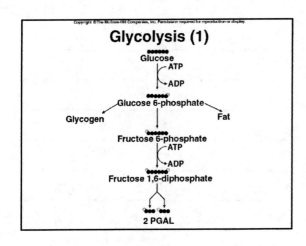

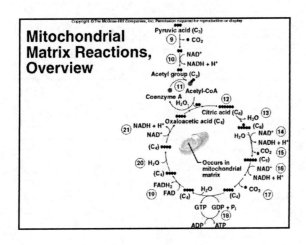

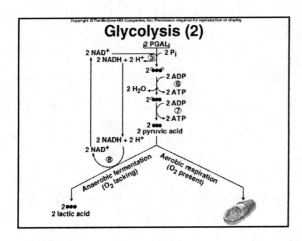

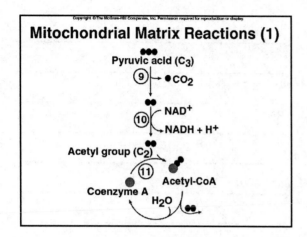

Mitochondrial Matrix Reactions (1)

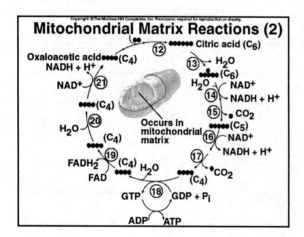

Mitochondrial Matrix Reactions (2)

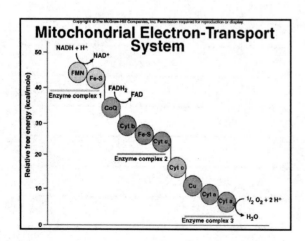

Mitochondrial Electron-Transport System

_____
_____
_____
_____
_____
_____

_____
_____
_____
_____
_____
_____

_____
_____
_____
_____
_____
_____

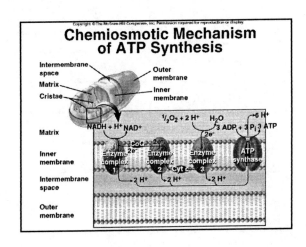

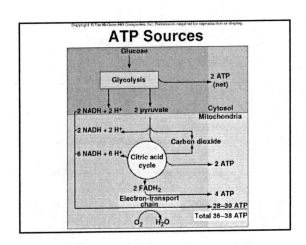

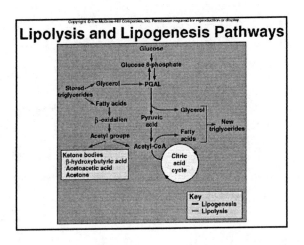

Amino Acid Metabolism Pathways

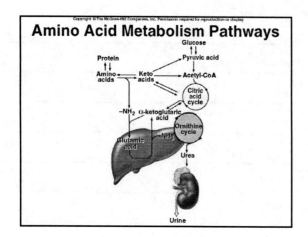

_____

_____

_____

_____

_____

_____

_____

Urea Synthesis

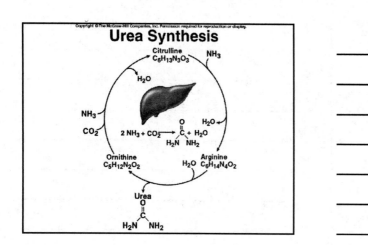

_____

_____

_____

_____

_____

_____

_____

Chapter 27

Anatomy and Physiology: The Unity of Form and Function

Second Edition

Kenneth S. Saladin

(c) The McGraw-Hill Companies, Inc.

Chromosomal Sex Determination

X

Sperm

X

Egg

⟶ XX = female

Y

Y

⟶ XY = male

Male Perineum

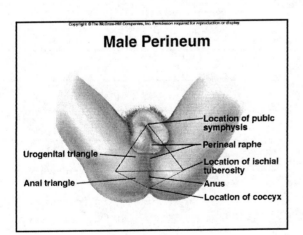

Urogenital triangle

Anal triangle

Location of pubic symphysis

Perineal raphe

Location of ischial tuberosity

Anus

Location of coccyx

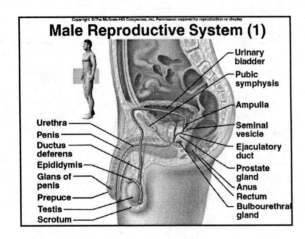

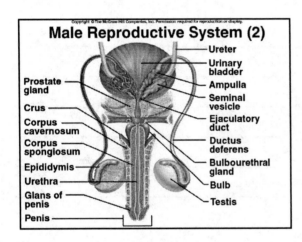

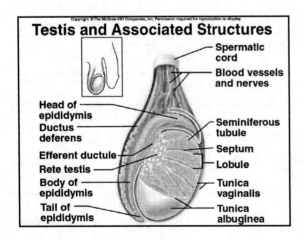

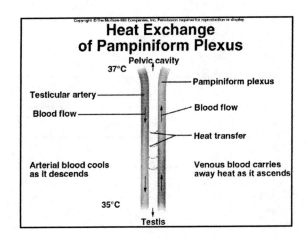

Heat Exchange of Pampiniform Plexus

Pelvic cavity

37°C

Testicular artery

Blood flow

Pampiniform plexus

Blood flow

Heat transfer

Arterial blood cools as it descends

Venous blood carries away heat as it ascends

35°C

Testis

_____
_____
_____
_____
_____
_____
_____

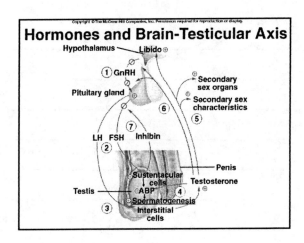

Hormones and Brain-Testicular Axis

Hypothalamus

Libido ⊕

① GnRH

Pituitary gland

Secondary sex organs

Secondary sex characteristics

⑤

⑥

⑦

LH FSH

Inhibin

②

Penis

Sustentacular cells

Testosterone

Testis

ABP

④

⊕

Spermatogenesis

③

Interstitial cells

_____
_____
_____
_____
_____
_____
_____

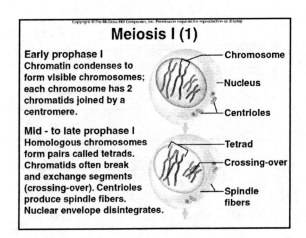

Meiosis I (1)

Early prophase I
Chromatin condenses to form visible chromosomes; each chromosome has 2 chromatids joined by a centromere.

Mid - to late prophase I
Homologous chromosomes form pairs called tetrads. Chromatids often break and exchange segments (crossing-over). Centrioles produce spindle fibers. Nuclear envelope disintegrates.

Chromosome

Nucleus

Centrioles

Tetrad

Crossing-over

Spindle fibers

_____
_____
_____
_____
_____
_____
_____

Meiosis I (2)

Metaphase I
Tetrads align on equatorial plane of cell with centromeres attached to spindle fibers.

Anaphase I
Homologous chromosomes separate and migrate to opposite poles of the cell.

Telophase I
New nuclear envelopes form around chromosomes; cell undergoes cytoplasmic division (cytokinesis). Each cell is now haploid.

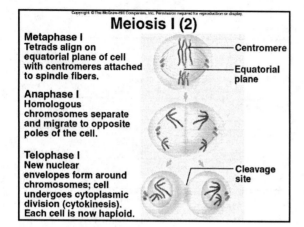

— Centromere
— Equatorial plane
— Cleavage site

Meiosis II (1)

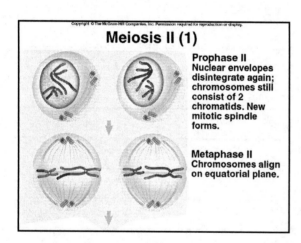

Prophase II
Nuclear envelopes disintegrate again; chromosomes still consist of 2 chromatids. New mitotic spindle forms.

Metaphase II
Chromosomes align on equatorial plane.

Meiosis II (2)

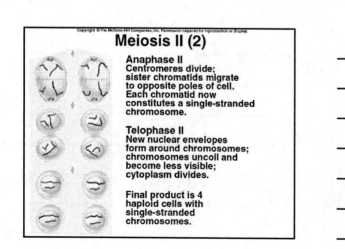

Anaphase II
Centromeres divide; sister chromatids migrate to opposite poles of cell. Each chromatid now constitutes a single-stranded chromosome.

Telophase II
New nuclear envelopes form around chromosomes; chromosomes uncoil and become less visible; cytoplasm divides.

Final product is 4 haploid cells with single-stranded chromosomes.

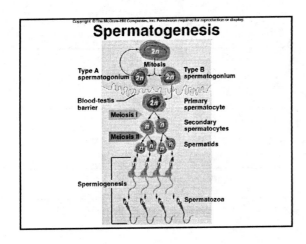

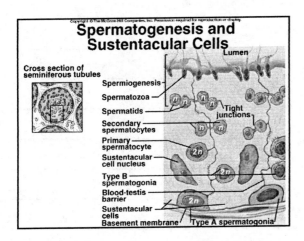

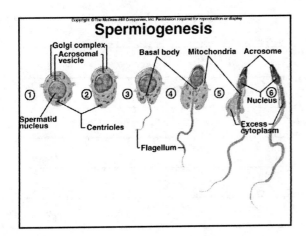

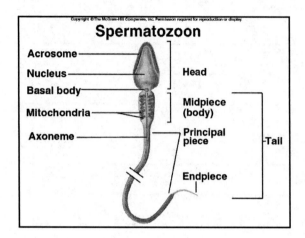

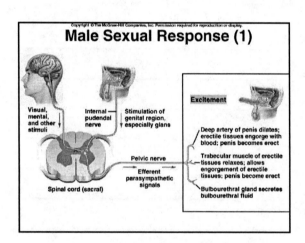

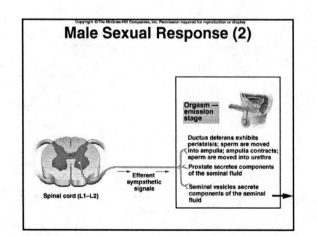

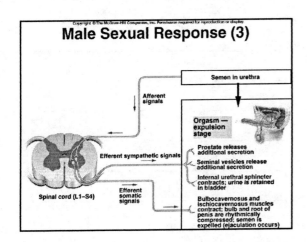

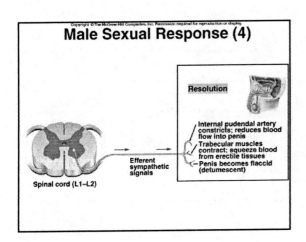

Chapter 28

Anatomy and Physiology: The Unity of Form and Function
Second Edition

Kenneth S. Saladin

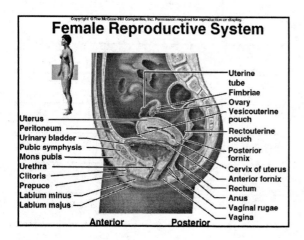

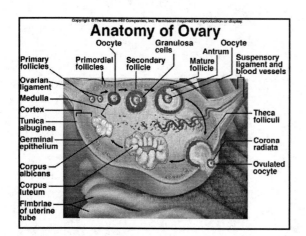

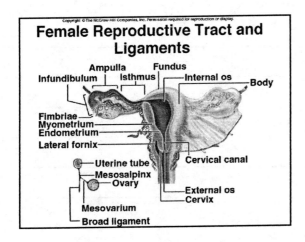

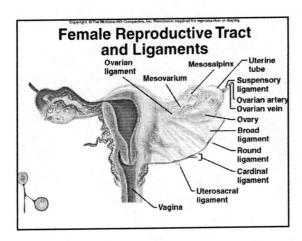

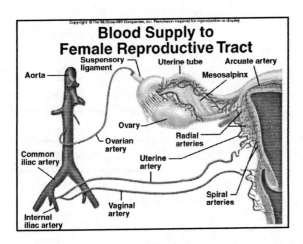

Female Perineum, Surface Anatomy

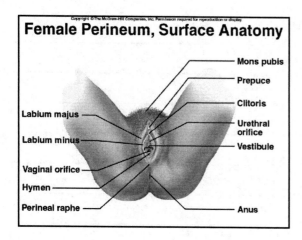

- Mons pubis
- Prepuce
- Clitoris
- Urethral orifice
- Vestibule
- Labium majus
- Labium minus
- Vaginal orifice
- Hymen
- Perineal raphe
- Anus

Female Perineum, Subcutaneous

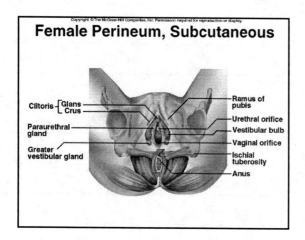

- Clitoris — Glans / Crus
- Paraurethral gland
- Greater vestibular gland
- Ramus of pubis
- Urethral orifice
- Vestibular bulb
- Vaginal orifice
- Ischial tuberosity
- Anus

Oogenesis and Follicle Development

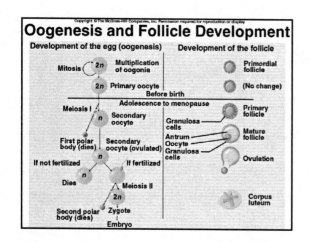

Development of the egg (oogenesis)

- Mitosis — Multiplication of oogonia (2n)
- Primary oocyte (2n)

Before birth

Adolescence to menopause

- Meiosis I — Secondary oocyte (n)
- First polar body (dies)
- Secondary oocyte (ovulated) (n)
- If not fertilized
- If fertilized
- Dies (n)
- Meiosis II
- Second polar body (dies)
- Zygote (2n)
- Embryo

Development of the follicle

- Primordial follicle
- (No change)
- Primary follicle
- Granulosa cells
- Mature follicle
- Antrum
- Oocyte
- Granulosa cells
- Ovulation
- Corpus luteum

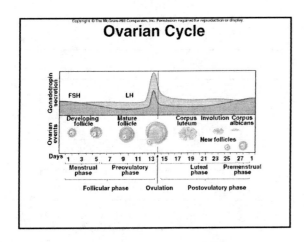

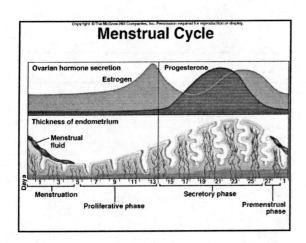

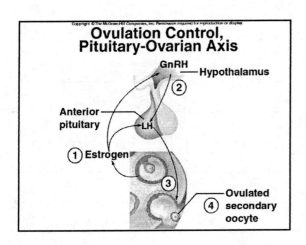

Hormone Levels and Pregnancy

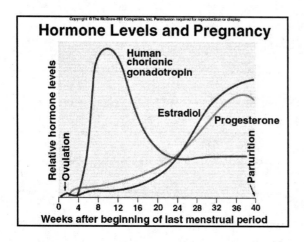

Relative hormone levels

Human chorionic gonadotropin

Estradiol

Progesterone

Ovulation

Parturition

0 4 8 12 16 20 24 28 32 36 40

Weeks after beginning of last menstrual period

_____

_____

_____

_____

_____

_____

Full-Term Fetus

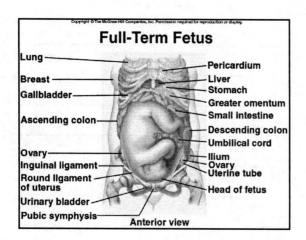

Lung

Breast

Gallbladder

Ascending colon

Ovary

Inguinal ligament

Round ligament of uterus

Urinary bladder

Pubic symphysis

Pericardium

Liver

Stomach

Greater omentum

Small intestine

Descending colon

Umbilical cord

Ilium

Ovary

Uterine tube

Head of fetus

Anterior view

_____

_____

_____

_____

_____

_____

Stages of Childbirth, Early Dilation

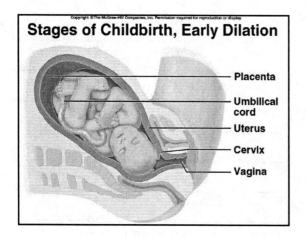

Placenta

Umbilical cord

Uterus

Cervix

Vagina

_____

_____

_____

_____

_____

_____

Stages of Childbirth, Late Dilation

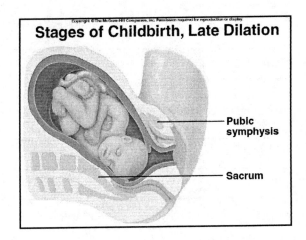

Pubic symphysis

Sacrum

Stages of Childbirth, Expulsion

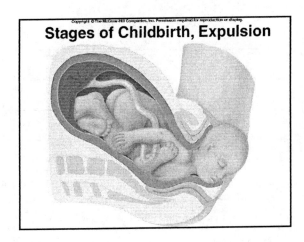

Stages of Childbirth, Placental Stage

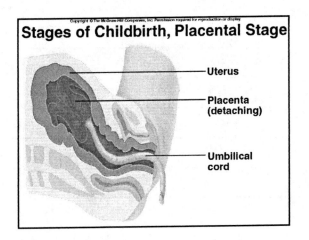

Uterus

Placenta (detaching)

Umbilical cord

Chapter 29

Anatomy and Physiology: The Unity of Form and Function
Second Edition

Kenneth S. Saladin

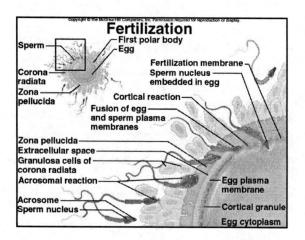

Fertilization

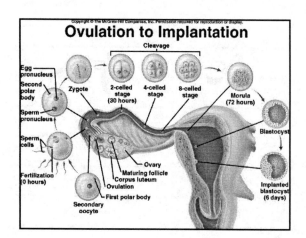

Ovulation to Implantation

Structure of Blastocyst

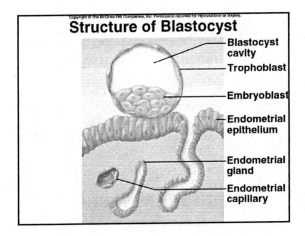

Copyright © The McGraw-Hill Companies, Inc. Permission required for reproduction or display.

- Blastocyst cavity
- Trophoblast
- Embryoblast
- Endometrial epithelium
- Endometrial gland
- Endometrial capillary

Early Implantation

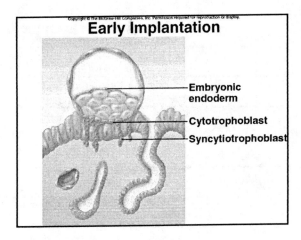

Copyright © The McGraw-Hill Companies, Inc. Permission required for reproduction or display.

- Embryonic endoderm
- Cytotrophoblast
- Syncytiotrophoblast

Implanted Conceptus at 2 Weeks

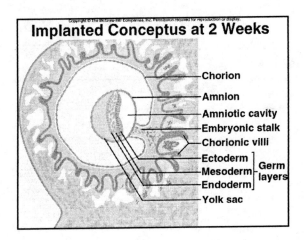

Copyright © The McGraw-Hill Companies, Inc. Permission required for reproduction or display.

- Chorion
- Amnion
- Amniotic cavity
- Embryonic stalk
- Chorionic villi
- Ectoderm ⎤
- Mesoderm ⎬ Germ layers
- Endoderm ⎦
- Yolk sac

195

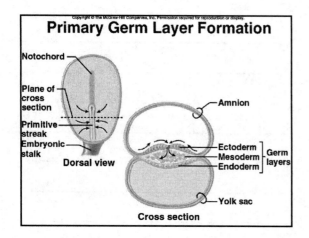

Primary Germ Layer Formation

Notochord

Plane of cross section

Primitive streak

Embryonic stalk

Dorsal view

Amnion

Ectoderm
Mesoderm
Endoderm
Germ layers

Yolk sac

Cross section

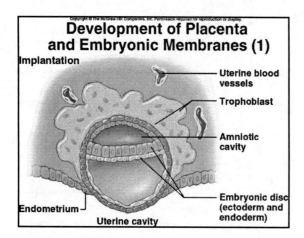

Development of Placenta and Embryonic Membranes (1)

Implantation

Uterine blood vessels

Trophoblast

Amniotic cavity

Endometrium

Uterine cavity

Embryonic disc (ectoderm and endoderm)

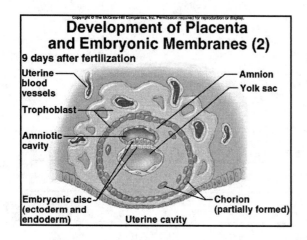

Development of Placenta and Embryonic Membranes (2)

9 days after fertilization

Uterine blood vessels

Trophoblast

Amniotic cavity

Embryonic disc (ectoderm and endoderm)

Amnion

Yolk sac

Chorion (partially formed)

Uterine cavity

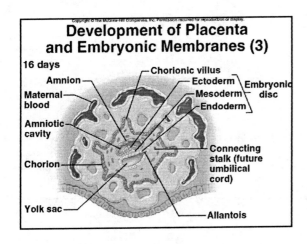

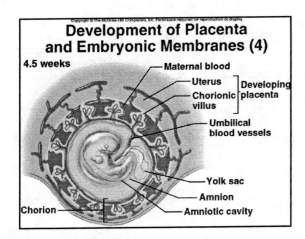

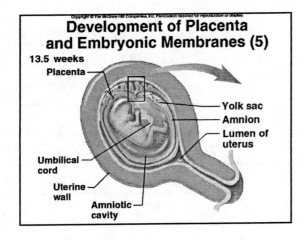

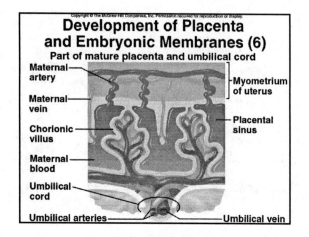

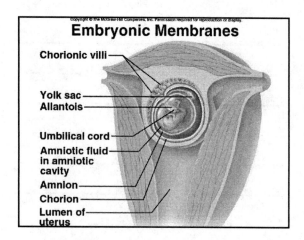

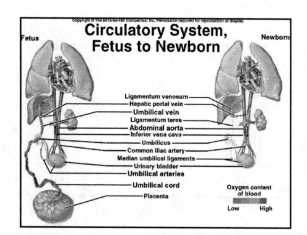

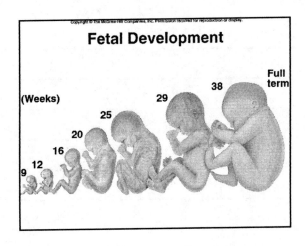

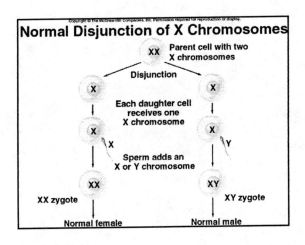

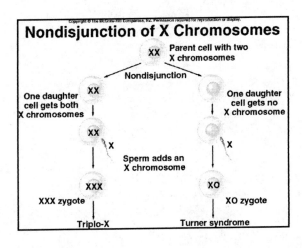

Down Syndrome Characteristics

Incurved finger

Single palmar ("simian") crease

Short broad hands

_____

_____

_____

_____

_____

_____

_____

ISBN 0-07-250103-0

90000>